SINGING on OUR WAY

ENLARGED EDITION

By   **LILLA BELLE PITTS**
Professor Emeritus of Music Education
Teachers College, Columbia University, New York

MABELLE GLENN
Formerly Director of Music
Public Schools, Kansas City, Missouri

LORRAIN E. WATTERS
Director of Music
Public Schools, Des Moines, Iowa

and   **LOUIS G. WERSEN**
Director of Music Education
Public Schools, Philadelphia, Pennsylvania

ILLUSTRATIONS BY Ruth Wood, Dorothy Grider,
Margo Pisillo, and Hertha Depper

GINN AND COMPANY

Contents

Acknowledgments

Acknowledgment is due to composers, authors, and publishers for permission to reprint songs and poems in this book, as follows:

Marjorie Barrows, "The Wind Elves," by Ruth Dixon; the Estate of Katharine Lee Bates, "America the Beautiful"; Behrman House, Inc., "Ku-ku-ri-ku!" from *Gateway to Jewish Song*, by Eisenstein; Blackwell & Mott, "The Scissor-Man," from *Fifty New Poems for Children*, by Madeline Nightingale, by permission of Basil Blackwell & Mott, Ltd., Oxford; Fannie R. Buchanan, "Good Morning, Sky"; Amelia Josephine Burr, "Rain in the Night"; The Curtis Publishing Company and the Author, "Father's Valentine," by Dorothy Langley, reprinted by special permission from *The Ladies' Home Journal*, copyright 1935, The Curtis Publishing Company; Mrs. Katherine H. Dent, "When You Send a Valentine" (words only), by Mildred J. Hill, from Emilie Poulsson's *Holiday Songs*; Doubleday & Company, "The Animal Store," from *Taxis and Toadstools*, by Rachel Field, copyright 1926, Doubleday & Company, Inc.; Follett Publishing Company, "Dive, Ducks, Dive," from *Around a Toadstool Table*, by Rowena Bastin Bennett; Ginn and Company, "The Bells" and "Morning Bells" from *Introductory Music* of The Music Education Series; Ginn and Company and the editors of The World of Music, "Fox and Goose," "Jack-o'-Lantern," "Little Ducky Duddle," "On a Rainy Day," "Pretty Girls and the Shoemaker," and "Round the Pear Tree," from *Listen and Sing*, copyright 1936, 1943, by Ginn and Company; "Fairy Voices," "The Fiddles," "Jingle at the Window," "Loving Care," and "Silver Bells," from *Tuning Up*, copyright 1936, 1943, by Ginn and Company; "Cats and Dogs," "Halloween," "Laughing Ho, Ho!" "Playing in the Sun," and "Work and Play," from *Rhythms and Rimes*, copyright 1936, 1943, by Ginn and Company; Harcourt, Brace and Company, lines from "Going Up to London" and "Spring Wind," from *Magpie Lane*, by Nancy Byrd Turner, copyright 1927 by Harcourt, Brace and Company, Inc.; Harper & Brothers, "Two Winds," from *A Pocketful of Rhymes*, by Mary Louise Allen, copyright 1939 by Harper & Brothers, and "Spring Rain," from *A World to Know*, by James S. Tippett, copyright 1933 by Harper & Brothers; Bruce Humphries, Inc., "New Shoes," from *Do You Remember?* by Marjorie Seymour Watts, copyright 1927, by The Four Seas Company, reprinted by permission of Bruce Humphries, Inc., Boston; Mr. and Mrs. Alden Arthur Knipe, "Autumn," from *Remember Rhymes*, by A. Arthur Knipe; Longmans, Green & Company, "A Getting-Up Song," "Widdy-Widdy-Wurky," and "Washing Day" ("Working Day"), from *Singing Circle*, by Lady Bell; Frank Luther, "Trip a Trop a Tronjes," from *Americans and Their Songs*; The Macmillan Company, "The Ballad of Downal Baun" (The Moon-Cradle's Rocking), from *Poems*, by Padraic Colum, copyright 1916, 1922, 1927, 1930, and 1932, The Macmillan Company; "Frolic" (excerpt), from *Collected Poems* by AE, copyright 1926, The Macmillan Company; lines from "Doorbells" and "A Summer Morning," from *Pointed People*, by Rachel Field, copyright 1924 and 1930, The Macmillan Company; "Here Is the Beehive," from *The Rooster Crows*, by the Petershams, copyright 1945, The Macmillan Company; "When I Was Young" (excerpt), from *Collected Poems*, by James Stephens, copyright 1909, 1912,

4

Can you sing?
I love to sing!
Music, like a bird in spring,
With a gold
And silver note
Gets into
My heart and throat.

Eleanor Farjeon

ABOUT SONGS WE KNOW

This Old Man

English Singing Game

CHORDS: F   F   B♭   C₇

1. This old man, he played one, He played nick-nack on my thumb;
2. This old man, he played two, He played nick-nack on my shoe;
3. This old man, he played three, He played nick-nack on my knee;

F   B♭   F   C₇   C₇   F

Nick-nack, pad-dy whack, Give a dog a bone, This old man came roll-ing home.

4. This old man, he played four,
   He played nick-nack on my door; *(forehead)*

5. This old man, he played five,
   He played nick-nack on my hive; *(fight bees)*

6. This old man, he played six,
   He played nick-nack on my sticks; *(index fingers)*

7. This old man, he played sev'n,
   He played nick-nack up in heav'n; *(fly like angels)*

8. This old man, he played eight,
   He played nick-nack on my pate; *(top of head)*

9. This old man, he played nine,
   He played nick-nack on my spine, *(between shoulders)*

10. This old man, he played ten,
    He played nick-nack once again;
    Nick-nack, paddy whack, Give a dog a bone,
    Now we'll all go running home.

There Was a Crooked Man

Mother Goose

Ethel Crowninshield

There was a crook-ed man, Who went a crook-ed mile

And found a crook-ed six-pence up - on a crook-ed stile.

He bought a crook-ed cat that caught a crook-ed mouse,

And they all lived to-geth-er in a lit-tle crook-ed house.

Eency, Weency Spider

Traditional

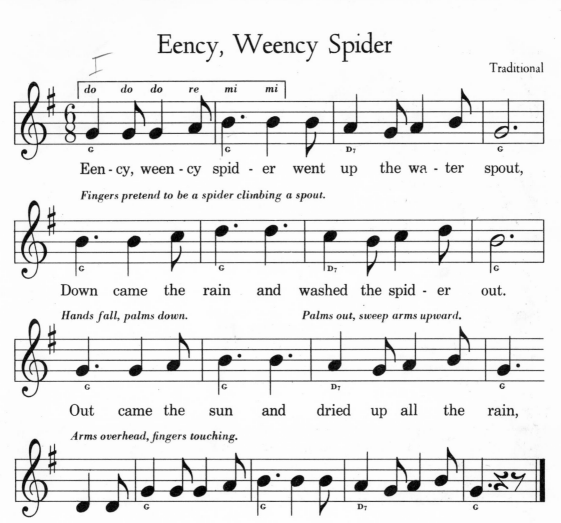

do do do re mi mi

Een-cy, ween-cy spid-er went up the wa-ter spout,

Fingers pretend to be a spider climbing a spout.

Down came the rain and washed the spid-er out.

Hands fall, palms down.   *Palms out, sweep arms upward.*

Out came the sun and dried up all the rain,

Arms overhead, fingers touching.

And the een-cy, ween-cy spid-er went up the spout a-gain.

Hands fall down and fingers climb spout again.

The Little Shoemaker

Alice C. D. Riley

Jessie L. Gaynor

1. There's a lit-tle wee man in a lit-tle wee house
2. He puts his nee-dle in and out,

Lives o-ver the way you see,
His thread flies to and fro,

And he sits at the win-dow and sews all day
With his ti-ny awl he bores the holes;

Mak-ing shoes for you and me.
Hear the ham-mer's bu-sy blow.

CHORUS

A - rap-a-tap - tap, a - rap-a-tap - tap,

Hear the ham - mer's tit - tat - tee.

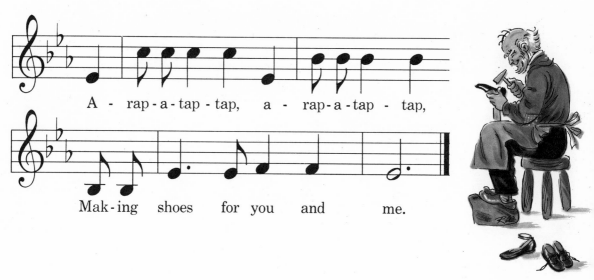

A - rap-a-tap-tap, a - rap-a-tap - tap,

Mak-ing shoes for you and me.

Sing a Song of Sixpence

Mother Goose

J. W. Elliott

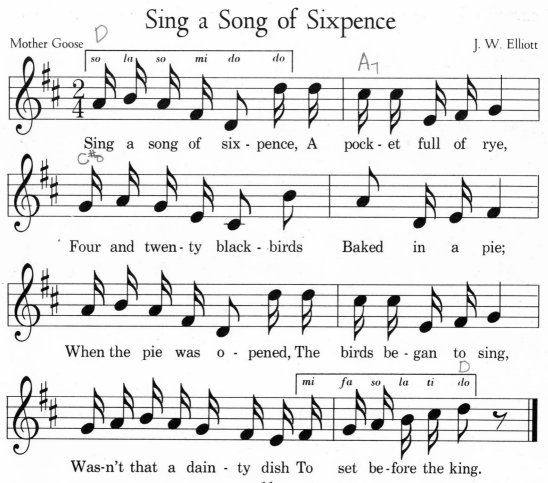

so la so mi do do

Sing a song of six - pence, A pock - et full of rye,

Four and twen - ty black - birds Baked in a pie;

When the pie was o - pened, The birds be - gan to sing,

mi fa so la ti do

Was-n't that a dain - ty dish To set be - fore the king.

11

Little Ducky Duddle

M. R.

Moiselle Renstrom

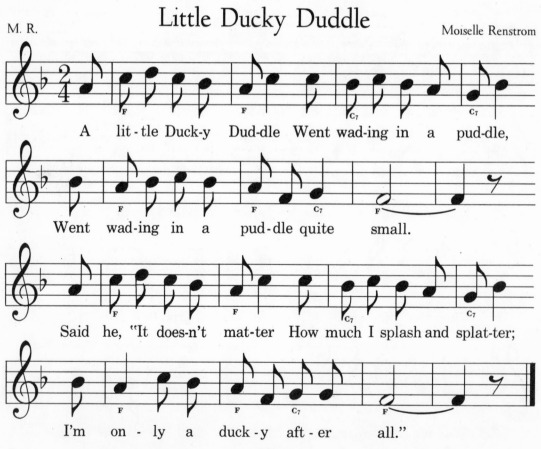

A lit-tle Duck-y Dud-dle Went wad-ing in a pud-dle,

Went wad-ing in a pud-dle quite small.

Said he, "It does-n't mat-ter How much I splash and splat-ter;

I'm on-ly a duck-y aft-er all."

12

Over in the Meadow

South Appalachian Folk Song

1. O - ver in the mead-ow in a nest in the tree,
2. O - ver in the hol - low in a pool in the bog,

mi mi re re do

Lived an old moth-er bird-ie and her lit - tle ba-bies three.
Lived an old moth-er frog-gie and her ba - by pol-li - wog.

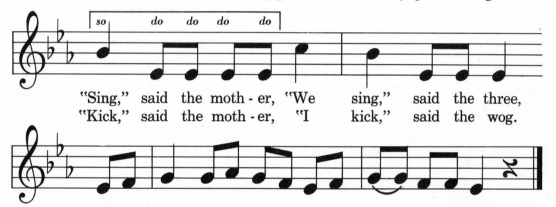

so do do do do

"Sing," said the moth - er, "We sing," said the three,
"Kick," said the moth - er, "I kick," said the wog.

And they sang and were hap-py in the nest · in the tree.
Then he kicked and he kicked him-self in-to a lit -tle frog.

Mary Had a Little Lamb

Sara J. Hale

Traditional

1. Ma-ry had a lit-tle lamb, lit-tle lamb, lit-tle lamb,
2. Ev-'ry-where that Ma-ry went, Ma-ry went, Ma-ry went,

Ma-ry had a lit-tle lamb, Its fleece was white as snow.
Ev-'ry-where that Ma-ry went, The lamb was sure to go.

How many of you can play this piece on the piano with both hands?

14

ABOUT FOLKS

Old folks, young folks,
Little folks too;
Mary Rose a-skipping
In a dress of blue.

Tall folks, short folks,
Children in between;
Johnny Jones a-jumping
In a sweater green.

Fat folks, thin folks,
Babies very sweet;
Boys and girls a-dancing
And laughing in the street.

Busy folks, lazy folks,
Children always gay;
Boys and girls a-growing
While singing at their play.

Anonymous

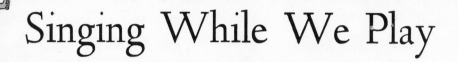

Singing While We Play

A hop, a skip, and off you go!
Happy heart and merry toe,
Up-and-down and in-and-out,
This way, that way, round about![1]

Eleanor Farjeon

Girls and Boys, Come Out to Play

English Singing Game

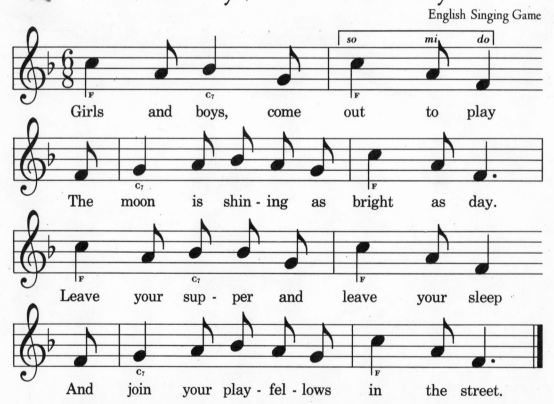

Girls and boys, come out to play

The moon is shin-ing as bright as day.

Leave your sup-per and leave your sleep

And join your play-fel-lows in the street.

[1] Reprinted by permission of the publishers, J. B. Lippincott Company, from "Dancing," in *Sing for Your Supper* by Eleanor Farjeon. Copyright, 1938, by Eleanor Farjeon.

When I am walking down the street
I do so like to watch my feet.
Perhaps you do not know the news:
Mother has bought me fine new shoes!
When the left one steps I do not speak,
I listen to its happy squeak.

Marjorie Seymour Watts

Running and Walking

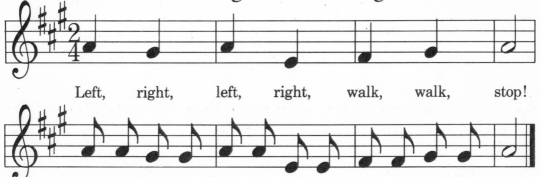

Left,   right,   left,   right,   walk,   walk,   stop!

Run-ning, run-ning, run-ning, run-ning, run-ning, run-ning, stop!

Skipping and Galloping

Skip-ping, skip - ping, skip - ping, skip - ping, skip - ping, skip - ping, stop!

Gal-lop-ing, gal-lop-ing, gal-lop-ing, gal-lop-ing, gal-lop-ing, gal-lop-ing, stop!

17

Run and Walk

Run, run, run, run, run, run, run, run, Run, run, run, run, run, run, run, run,

Walk, walk, walk, walk, Walk, walk, walk, walk,

Run, run, run, run, run, run, run, run, Run, run, run, run, run, run, run, run,

Walk, walk, walk, walk, Walk, walk, stop!

Listen to "Ballet Music," Gluck. (Victor Rhythm Album One.)

18

Skipping and Walking

Skip-ty, skip-ty, skip-ty, skip-ty, Skip-ty, skip-ty, skip-ty, skip-ty,

Walk, walk, walk, walk, Walk, walk, walk, walk,

Skip-ty, skip-ty, skip-ty, skip-ty, Skip-ty, skip-ty, skip-ty, skip-ty,

Walk, walk, walk, walk, Walk, walk, stop!

Hippety Hop

Traditional

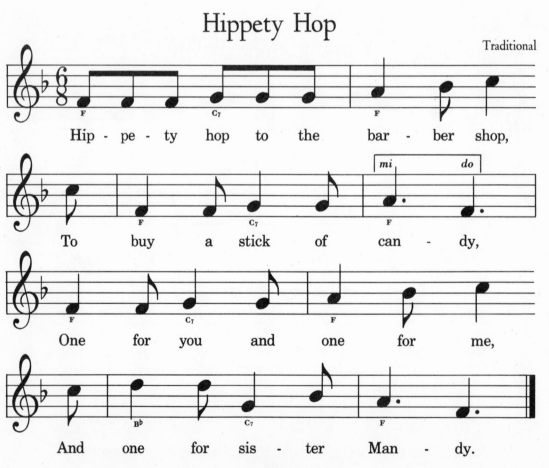

Hip - pe - ty hop to the bar - ber shop,

To buy a stick of can - dy,

One for you and one for me,

And one for sis - ter Man - dy.

Penny Problems

John Farrar

Charles J. Cromwell

Four bright win-dows where the street-car stops,

Oh lol-ly-pops! Oh lol-ly-pops!

And two-for-a-pen-ny lem-on drops;

Such fas-ci-nat-ing can-dy shops!

slower
mi re do

Four bright win-dows where the street-car stops!

When We Go to Play

English

so so la so so la so so mi

1. What shall we take when we go to play, go to play, go to play,
2. We will · take our · bat and ball, bat and ball, bat and ball,
3. We will · take our · bi - cy - cles, bi - cy - cles, bi - cy - cles,

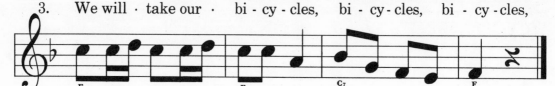

What shall we take when we go to play, when we go to play?
We will · take our · bat and ball when we go to play.
We will · take our · bi - cy - cles, when we go to play.

4. We will take our roller skates, etc.
5. We will take our rolling hoops, etc.
6. We will take our jumping ropes, etc.

Here We Go Skating Along

L. B. P.

French Folk Tune

Here we go skat - ing a - long in a row,

Skat - ing and skat - ing and skat - ing we go.

Now we go skat - ing a - round and a - round,

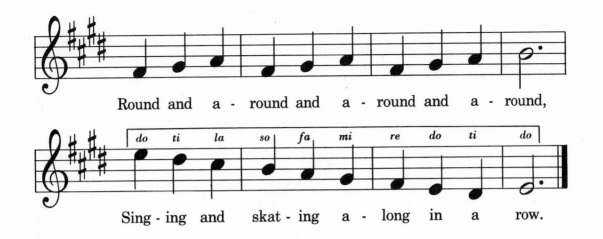

Round and a-round and a-round and a-round,

Sing-ing and skat-ing a-long in a row.

do ti la so fa mi re do ti do

We're Riding Our Bicycles

Children's Song

so so mi so so mi so

We're rid-ing our bi-cy-cles, rid-ing our bi-cy-cles,

do ti la so

Round and a-round, round and a-round.

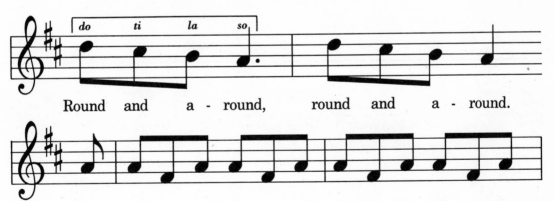

We're rid-ing our bi-cy-cles, rid-ing our bi-cy-cles,

fa mi re do

Round and a-round, round and a-round.

Bring the Bat

L. B. P.

L. B. P.

do re mi fa so la so

Bring the bat and bring the ball, Bring your hoops and skates and all.

Let us make a mer-ry ring, Round the cir-cle we'll dance and sing.

fa mi re do

Hur-ry, hur-ry, come and play For it is a hol-i-day.

Come with Me

M. M.

Marian Major

do re mi

1. Come with me, let's go skat-ing, skat-ing;
2. Come with me, let's go skat-ing, skat-ing;

mi re do

Come with me, let us skate to-day.
Come with me, we will skate a-way.

Listen to "Skating," Kullak. (Victor Rhythm Album Two.)

24

Riding Our Bicycles

S. C.

Susan Castle

so do mi so do mi so

1. We're rid - ing and rid - ing and rid - ing a - round,
2. Our feet on the ped - als, our hands on the bars,

so la ti do

Rid - ing our bi - cy - cles all round the town.
When we are rid - ing we look out for cars.

Balloons

Meadowbrook
School Children

do do

Bal - loon! Bal - loon! Come buy your bal - loon!

Red, white and blue, Here's one for you.

Bal - loon! Bal - loon! Come buy your bal - loon!

Listen to "Waltz No. 2," Brahms. (Victor Rhythm Album Two.)

Swing High, Swing Low

Alice B. Haines

Louella Garrett

Swing · high, swing low, swing · high, swing low,

First up in the tree-tops a - sail-ing we go!

Then down to the ground where the soft grass-es grow.

Swing · high, swing low, swing · high, swing · low!

Swinging and Singing

W. B.

Winifred Bodie

Swing-ing, swing-ing, swing-ing, 'way up in the sky;

Swing-ing, here we go swing-ing, reach-ing for clouds up on high.

Here we go swing-ing as we sing,

swing-ing and sing-ing in our swing.

Come Along and Join Our Song

L. B. P.

L. B. P.

do do do re mi fa so so

Come a-long and join our sing-ing, Come a-long and join our song,

so la so fa mi re do

Tir-ra-lir-ra-lir-ra-lir-ra, Tir-ra-lir-ra is our song.

27

Tramping and Stamping

L. B. P.

Dutch Folk Tune

A - tramp-ing, stamp-ing here we come

As we keep time to our drum, drum, drum;

A - tramp-ing, stamp-ing here we come

As we keep time to our drum, drum, drum;

A - march-ing, march-ing in a row,

We whirl our drum-sticks as we go.

Rom, tom, tom, · trrr - rom - pi - ty tom - ty tom, tom, tom;

Rom, tom, tom, · trrr - rom - pi - ty tom, tom, tom, tom, tom!

Listen to "March," Bach-MacDowell. (Victor Rhythm Album Three.)

Sing a Song of Merry-Go-Round

Mother Goose

Ethel Anthony

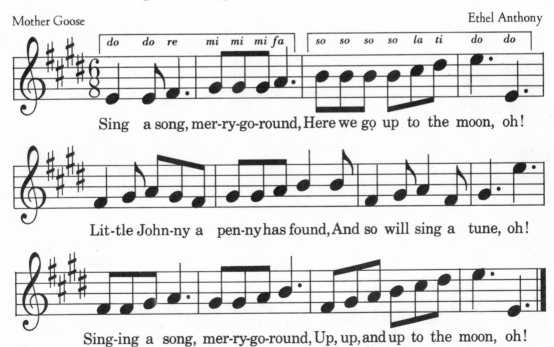

do   do   re   mi   mi   mi   fa   *so   so   so   so   la   ti   do   do*

Sing   a song, mer-ry-go-round, Here we go up to the moon, oh!

Lit-tle John-ny a   pen-ny has found, And so will sing a   tune, oh!

Sing-ing a song, mer-ry-go-round, Up, up, and up to the moon, oh!

Listen to "Galloping Horses," Anderson. (Victor Rhythm Album One.)

Who Are You?

Tone-matching Song

Knock, knock, knock! Who are you? I am Kate! Please come in.
Charles!

(Here are some names that will help you to fit your name to this song.)

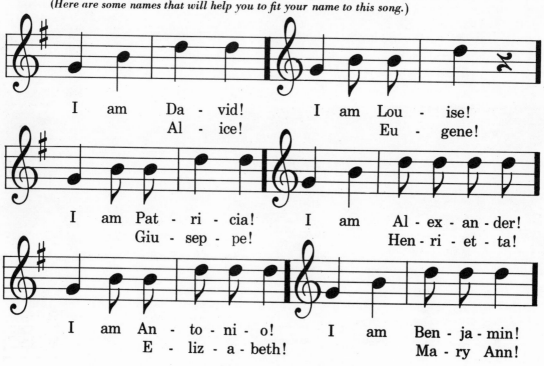

I am Da - vid!   I am Lou - ise!
Al - ice!   Eu - gene!

I am Pat - ri - cia!   I am Al - ex - an - der!
Giu - sep - pe!   Hen - ri - et - ta!

I am An - to - ni - o!   I am Ben - ja - min!
E - liz - a - beth!   Ma - ry Ann!

Jerry Hall

Nursery Rhyme   Barry S. Brinsmaid

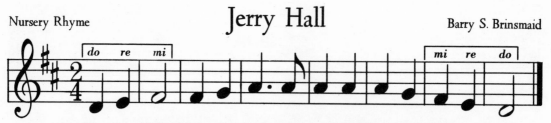

Jer - ry Hall, he's so small, A mouse could eat him, hat and all!

See if you can make a rhyme with your name.

30

Singing Games

Someday I think I'll travel 'round
And visit every land
And learn to speak the language that
Each child can understand.

They'll teach me how to play their games
And, if they want me to,
I'll show them diff'rent kinds of tricks
That I know how to do.

They'll want to ask me questions then,
And I will ask them others,
Until at last we understand
Like sisters and like brothers.

Helen Wing

Round and Round the Village

English Singing Game

1. Round and round the vil-lage, Round and round the vil-lage,
Round and round the vil-lage, As we have done be-fore.

2. In and out the windows, etc.
3. Stand before your playmate, etc.
4. Shake his hand and leave him, etc.
5. Follow me to London, etc.

31

Looking for a Partner

Danish Folk Tune

How many times can you find this pattern?

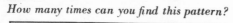
so do re mi fa so mi

mi re do

This girl is slow-ly walk-ing, is slow-ly walk-ing round the ring,

She's look-ing for a part-ner with whom to dance and sing,

She stands before partner.

Then hop-san-sa, tra la la, la, la, then hop-san-sa, tra la la, la, la!

All couples lock right elbows and swing.   *Lock left elbows and swing.*

And now she has a part-ner with whom to dance and sing.

Girl without a partner walks into center of ring and game begins again.

Draw a Bucket of Water

English Singing Game

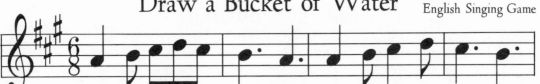

Draw a buck-et of wa - ter, For my la - dy's daugh - ter,

Couple, with hands joined, form arch. Arms pump up and down as children pass under arch.

so fa mi re do

One a skip, two a jump, Please, Ted-dy boy, duck un-der the pump!
Sal - ly girl,

First two caught form next arch.

Turning, Turning 'Round

Free translation

Italian Singing Game

so so la la so mi

1. Turn-ing, turn-ing 'round, we're turn-ing round and round.
2. Turn-ing, turn-ing 'round, we're turn-ing round and round.

Make a ring and move around.

Now give to her who wants it a lit - tle bunch of po - sies.
Now give to him who wants it a lit - tle stick of can - dy.

Child in center looks for "the one she loves." la so fa fa mi re do

San - dri - na takes the po - sies and bows to the one she loves.
Giu - sep - pe takes the can - dy and bows to the one he loves.

Child bows before "the one she loves." Chosen child takes place in center of ring.

Listen to "Ring Around the Rosy" from *Memories of Childhood*, Pinto.
(Victor Listening Album One.)

Bluebird, Bluebird

Folk Game (Texas style)

so mi so mi so la so mi

Blue-bird, blue-bird through my win-dow, Blue-bird, blue-bird through my win-dow,

*Stand in circle, hands joined and held high to form windows. Child who is bluebird
flies in and out windows.*

Blue-bird, blue-bird through my win-dow, Oh, John-ny, aren't you tired?

Take a lit - tle girl and tap her on the shoul - der,
boy   him

Bluebird taps partner on shoulder.   *These two fly in and out the windows.*

Take a lit - tle girl and tap her on the shoul - der,
boy   him

Take a lit - tle girl and tap her on the shoul - der,
boy   him

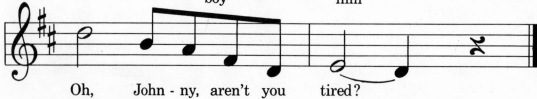

Oh, John - ny, aren't you tired?

*The second time the song is sung the two bluebirds choose new partners, the third time four
bluebirds and so on.*

34

Jenny, Come Tie My Tie

English Singing Game

BOYS

Jen-ny, come tie my, Jen-ny, come tie my,

Line of boys, with their hands pretending to catch loose ends of neckties, move toward line of girls.

Jen - ny, come tie my new neck - tie.

GIRLS

I've tied it be - hind, I've tied it be - fore,

As girls move forward, boys move backward. Girls pretend to tie the neckties front and back.

I've tied it so much, I'll tie it no more.

Girls walk backward. A sharp glancing clap says, "We're through trying."

Fox and Goose

Translation by Beatrice Wadhams

Swedish Singing Game

do do re mi fa so so mi do

1. Fox sit-ting on a chair, on a chair, Tag me, Fox-y Mis - ter!
2. Fox wait-ing for a goose, for a goose, You won't find an-oth - er;

You are clev - er, but you nev-er Catch me or my sis - ter!
Fox - y wink-ing, fox - y blink-ing, Will you catch my broth-er?

35

Looby Loo

English Singing Game

Now we dance loo-by loo, · Now we dance loo-by light, ·

_so la so fa mi re do_

Now we dance loo-by loo, · All on a Sat-ur-day night. ·

1. I put my right hand in, · I take my right hand out, ·
2. I put my left hand in, · I take my left hand out, ·
3. I put my right foot in, · I take my right foot out, ·

I give my hand a shake, shake, shake, And turn my-self a-bout. ·
I give my hand a shake, shake, shake, And turn my-self a-bout. ·
I give my foot a shake, shake, shake, And turn my-self a-bout. ·

4. I put my left foot in,
I take my left foot out,
I give my foot a shake, shake, shake,
And turn myself about.

5. I put my whole self in,
I take my whole self out,
I give myself a shake, shake, shake,
And turn myself about.

Who Has the Button?

V. M. S.

Verna Meade Surer

But-ton, but-ton, who has the but-ton? Oh, where can it be?

I have to find it, I have to find it, If I could on-ly see.

John-ny holds his hands so tight, Ma-ry will not tell,

Jim-my looks as though he might, They're hid-ing it so well,

But-ton, but-ton, who has the but-ton? Oh, where can it be?

London Bridge

Singing Game

so   la   so   fa   mi   fa   so

1. Lon-don bridge is fall-ing down, fall-ing down, fall-ing down,
2. Build it up with i-ron bars, i-ron bars, i-ron bars,

Lon-don bridge is fall-ing down, My fair la-dy.
Build it up with i-ron bars, My fair la-dy.

One, Two, Three

Ethel Crowninshield   Brazilian Singing Game

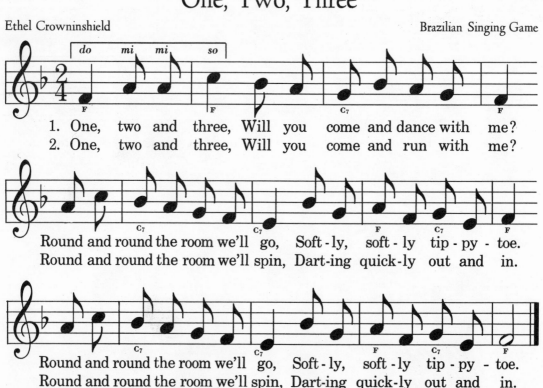

do   mi   mi   so

1. One, two and three, Will you come and dance with me?
2. One, two and three, Will you come and run with me?

Round and round the room we'll go, Soft-ly, soft-ly tip-py-toe.
Round and round the room we'll spin, Dart-ing quick-ly out and in.

Round and round the room we'll go, Soft-ly, soft-ly tip-py-toe.
Round and round the room we'll spin, Dart-ing quick-ly out and in.

Jingle at the Windows

Traditional Singing Game

Pass one win-dow, ti - de - o, Pass two win-dows, ti - de - o,

Single circle of partners, each child's left hand on right shoulder of child ahead. Group moves in circle.

mi re do

Pass three win-dows, ti - de - o, Jin-gle at the win-dows, ti - de - o.

Ti - de - o, ti - de - o, Jin-gle at the win-dows, ti - de - o,

Boy locks right elbow with girl behind him and swings.

Ti - de - o, ti - de - o, Jin-gle at the win-dows, ti - de - o.

Lock left elbows and swing.

39

Counting Songs

One, Two, Buckle My Shoe

Scale Song

1. One, two, buck-le my shoe; Three, four, shut the door;
2. Do, re, hur-ry let's play; Mi, fa, ask your Ma;

Five, six, pick up sticks; Sev'n, eight, lay them straight.
So, la, ask your Pa; Ti, do, then we'll go.

Eight, sev'n, six, five, four, three, two, one.
Do, ti, la, so, fa, mi, re, do.

One, Two, Three, Four

J. H.

Joan Henry

1. Do, re, mi, fa, so, A - fish - ing we will go;
2. One, two, three, four, five, I've caught a fish a - live;

La, ti, do, re, mi, A - sail - ing o'er the sea.
Six, sev'n, eight, nine, ten, I'll throw him in a - gain.

One Potato, Two Potatoes

Children's Chant

One po - ta - to, two po - ta - toes, three po - ta - toes, four, ·

Five po - ta - toes, six po - ta - toes, sev'n po - ta - toes, more. ·

Eight po - ta - toes, sev'n po - ta - toes, six po - ta - toes, five,

Four po - ta - toes, three po - ta - toes, two po - ta - toes, My, oh my!

Hot po - ta - toes!

John Brown Had a Little Indian

Traditional

John Brown had a lit-tle In-dian, John Brown had a lit-tle In-dian,

John Brown had a lit-tle In-dian, One lit-tle In-dian boy.

One lit - tle, two lit - tle, three lit - tle In - dians,
Ten lit - tle, nine lit - tle, eight lit - tle In - dians,

Four lit - tle, five lit - tle, six lit - tle In - dians,
Sev'n lit - tle, six lit - tle, five lit - tle In - dians,

Sev'n lit - tle, eight lit - tle, nine lit - tle In - dians,
Four lit - tle, three lit - tle, two lit - tle In - dians,

Ten lit - tle In - dian boys.
One lit - tle In - dian boy.

Here Is the Beehive

Traditional

Here is the bee-hive, where are the bees?

Fist, with thumb enclosed, is hive.

Hid-den a-way where no-bod-y sees.

Watch and you'll see them come out of the hive, One, two, three, four, five.

Pretend to watch hive.

Very slowly, beginning with thumb, fingers come out of the hive one by one; then all fly away.

43

Singing as We Work

Oh, When I Go a-Ploughing

English Singing Game

so do re mi fa so mi

1. Oh, when I go a-plough-ing, a - plough-ing, a - plough-ing,
Oh, when I go a-plough-ing, it's this way and that.
It's this way and that way, it's this way and that way,
Oh, when I go a-plough-ing, it's this way and that.

2. Oh, when I go a-raking, a-raking, a-raking, etc.
3. Oh, when I go a-planting, a-planting, a-planting, etc.
4. Oh, when I go a-hoeing, a-hoeing, a-hoeing, etc.

44

Hot Cross Buns

Traditional

mi re do

Hot   cross   buns!   Hot   cross   buns!

One a pen-ny, two a pen-ny, Hot cross buns!

Bake a Cake

Translated   German

so   so   la   la   so   so   mi

CHILD: Bak-er, I must bake a cake, Tell me what to do.

BAKER: Mix up good things in a bowl. Here is what they are:

Eggs and fat,   but-ter and salt, milk and flour,

Sug-ar makes the cake taste sweet, Put it in the ov-en.

The Broom

Carl Reinecke

so do so do mi do mi so so so so

Come tell me, come tell me! What use is the broom?

To sweep the rooms and kitch - en, To sweep the rooms and kitch-en.

Work and Play

M. A. L. Lane

Czechoslovakian Folk Tune

Cling, clang, cling, clang! Hear the an - vils ring!

Cling, clang, cling, clang! Clear the tones they sing!

Cling, clang, cling, clang! All the sum - mer day.

Cling, clang, cling, clang! While we work a - way!

Listen to "The Blacksmith," Brahms. (Victor Rhythm Album Three.)

Working Day

Lady Bell

From "Singing Circle"

do re mi mi mi mi fa fa fa

1. It was on a cold De-cem-ber morn As all in bed we lay,
2. It was on a cold De-cem-ber morn As all in bed we lay,

la so so mi re do

The bell did ring and say get up, It is our wash-ing day,
The bell did ring and say get up, It is our sweep-ing day,

For it's rub, rub, splash, splash, splash, splash a - way.
For it's sweep, sweep, dust, dust, dust, dust a - way.

We're all at work a - bout the house Up - on a wash-ing day.
We're all at work a - bout the house Up - on a sweep-ing day.

3. It was on a warm and sunny morn
As all in bed we lay,
The bell did ring and say get up,
It is our mowing day,
For it's mow, mow, mow, mow, mow,
   mow the hay.
We're all at work about the field
Upon a mowing day.

4. It was on a warm and sunny morn
As all in bed we lay,
The bell did ring and say get up,
It is our raking day,
For it's rake, rake, rake, rake, rake,
   rake the hay.
We're all at work about the field
Upon a raking day.

Our Family

Hundreds of dewdrops to greet the dawn,
Hundreds of lambs in the purple clover;
Hundreds of butterflies on the lawn,
But only one mother the wide world over.

George Cooper

The Carrier Pigeon

German Folk Song

1. I'm a car - ri - er   pi - geon, I can fly straight and true,
2. Fly-ing fast - er   and   fast-er, Through the rain and the   snow,

I shall bring to   your moth - er, Lov-ing words right from   you.
I have car - ried   the   mes - sage, It was wel-come, I   know.

Ada Lorraine Jex

Father's Birthday

Sue Hanlin

1. When Fa-ther's birth-day comes a-round, We bake the big-gest cake!
2. For Moth-er says he works all day To buy us ev - 'ry - thing!

We sift and whip and sweet-en it; Such trou-ble as we take.
So when we make his birth-day cake, Of course we laugh and sing.

When Grandmother comes to our house,
She sits in the chair and sews away.
She cuts some pieces just alike
And makes a quilt all day.

Elizabeth Madox Roberts

Grandmother

Miriam Ott Munson

Marian Deere

Grand-moth-er's gar-den had old-fash-ioned flow-ers,

Hol-ly-hocks, ros-es and rue,

And Grand-moth-er dear, in her quaint lit-tle gown,

Was an old-fash-ioned, sweet flow'r too.

Getting Up

From breakfast on through all the day.

R. L. S.

The Wake-Up Clock

Graham Haswell

do   re   mi   fa   so   so   so   so   fa   fa   mi   mi   re

All night long I tick, tick, tick So soft-ly no one hears,
Rhythm sticks.

But soon the night-time goes a-way And day-time light ap-pears.

'Tis then I ring my wake-up song So ev-'ry-bod-y hears.

so   la   la   ti   ti   do

I ring ding-a-ling, ding-a-ling, ling, ling, Wake up, wake up, my dears!
Triangle.

50

Lazy Mary, Will You Get Up

Singing Game

1. La-zy Ma-ry, will you get up, Will you get up, will you get up,
2. Oh no, moth-er, I won't get up, I won't get up, I won't get up,

La-zy Ma-ry, will you get up, Will you get up to-day?
Oh no, moth-er, I won't get up, I won't get up to-day.

Are You Sleeping?

Old French Round

Are you sleep-ing, are you sleep-ing, Broth-er John, Broth-er John?

Morn-ing bells are ring - ing, morn-ing bells are ring - ing,

Ding, dong, ding, ding, dong, ding.

51

Playing with Baby

Two little eyes to open and close,
Two little ears and one little nose,
Two little elbows, dimpled and sweet,
Two little shoes and two little feet,
Two little lips and one little chin,
Two little cheeks with a rose shut in;
Two little shoulders chubby and strong,
Two little legs running all day long.

The Pat-a-Cake Man

Meadowbrook
School Children

Pat - a - cake, pat - a - cake bak - er's man.

What be - came of the pat - a - cake man?

He slipped and fell right in - to the pan,

That's what hap - pened to the pat - a - cake man.

I'll Buy an Egg

Nursery Rhyme

Finger Play

Walter Howland

"I'll buy an egg," says <u>this</u> chick-ie;

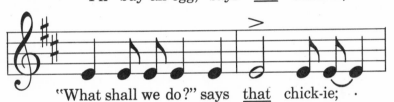

"What shall we do?" says <u>that</u> chick-ie;

"I'll cook it well," says <u>this</u> chick-ie;

"I'll salt it now," says <u>that</u> chick-ie;

"I'll eat it up," says <u>this</u> chick-ie.

53

Trip a Trop a Tronjes

New York Dutch

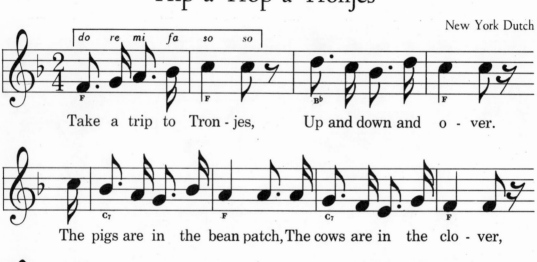

_do re mi fa so so_

Take a trip to Tron - jes,   Up and down and   o - ver.

The pigs are in the bean patch, The cows are in the clo - ver,

The ducks are in the wa-ter place, The calf is in the long grass.

_fa mi re do_

So big my ba - by is,   Pop - pe - jay   vas.[1]

[1] Dutch pet name.

54

Trot Along, My Little Mule

Paraphrase

Basque Foot-riding Song

Trot a-long, my lit-tle mule, Soon we will ar-rive in Soule.

What will you bring back from there? Nice new shoes and rock-ing chair. For

whom will these fine pres-ents be? For this good boy up-on my knee.

"Come, little child, cuddle close to me."

Eugene Field

Bye, Bye, Rock-a-Bye

French Lullaby

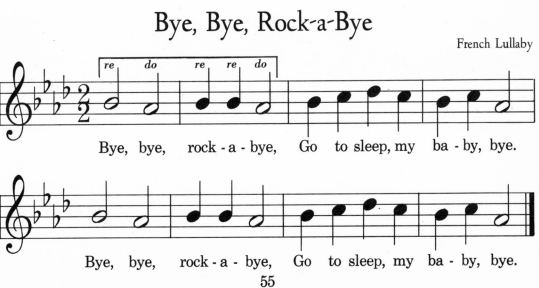

Bye, bye, rock-a-bye, Go to sleep, my ba-by, bye.

Bye, bye, rock-a-bye, Go to sleep, my ba-by, bye.

Berceuse

Alexander Ilyinsky, Op. 13

Watch these notes as you listen to the record. (Victor Rhythm Album Three.)

Hush, My Baby

Mississippi Lullaby

Hush, my ba - by, don't you cry, Dad-dy's going to come home by and by.

He will bring to his dear lit - tle ba - by

Can - dy and a kit - ty and a pup - py dog may - be.

Slower and very softly

Hush, hush, hush and don't you cry, Dad-dy's going to come home by and by.

French Cradle Song

French Folk Song

mi re do do re do re mi do

Go to sleep, my dear lit-tle broth-er,

Go to sleep, my lit-tle Pier-rot;

mi fa so re

Moth-er will watch, ten-der-ly near,

Fa-ther will come when the eve-ning is here,

Go to sleep, my dear lit-tle broth-er,

Go to sleep, my lit-tle Pier-rot.

Listen to "Sleeping Time" from *Memories of Childhood*, Pinto. (Victor Listening Album One.)

Sleepy Song

Anonymous

1. Lull - a - by, lull - a - by, Do not wake and weep,
2. Lull - a - by, lull - a - by, Lov - ing watch we keep,

Soft - ly in the cra - dle lie, Sleep, O sleep;
Soft - ly in the cra - dle lie, Sleep, O sleep;

Soft - ly in the cra - dle lie, Sleep, O sleep.
Soft - ly in the cra - dle lie, Sleep, O sleep.

Cradle Song

Miska Hauser, Op. 11

Watch these notes as you listen to the record. (Victor Rhythm Album Three.)

Winky, Blinky

New England Lullaby

L. B. P.

so so mi mi mi so so so mi

1. Wink - y, Blink - y, Nid - dy Nod!
2. Cud - dle, cud - dle, the wind's in the trees,

Fa - ther is fish - ing off Cape Cod.
Broth-er is sail - ing o'er the seas.

Wink - y, Blink - y, sleep - y eyes,
Nid - dy, Nod - dy, up and down,

mi re do

Moth - er is mak - ing ap - ple pies.
Sis - ter is mak-ing a vel - vet gown.

Lullaby

Ukrainian

am   dm   am   dm   am   dm

Lull - a - by, my ba - by, go to · sleep and · dream of chicks

am   dm   am   dm   am

And · lit-tle yel-low duck-lings, Go to sleep, my · ba - by dear.

Listen to "Berceuse," Järnefelt. (Victor Listening Album Two.)

Bedtime

G. H.

Graham Haswell

1, 2, 3, 4, 5, 6, 7, 8, Hur-ry to bed, it's get-ting late.

1, 2, 3, 4, 5, 6, 7, 8, Bet-ter hur-ry up; it's get-ting late.

Quiet Is the Night

Old Rhyme

Henry M. Halvorson

Qui - et is the night, soft is the breeze,

Dim is the moon · o - ver the trees.

Sleep, chil-dren, sleep, be not a - larmed,

An - gels on guard shall keep you un-harmed.

60

Father, Lead Me Day By Day

John P. Hopps

George C. Strattner

Fa-ther, lead me day · by day, Ev - er in Thine own·strong way;

Teach me to be pure and true, Show me what · I ought to do.

A Little Tune

Robert Schumann, Op. 68

How many of you can play this piece on the piano with both hands?

Now I Lay Me Down To Sleep

Anonymous

John Langland

Andante cantabile

Now I lay me down to sleep,

I pray Thee, Lord, my soul to keep.

Thy love go with me all the night,

And wake me with the morn - ing light.

Loving Care

Nellie Poorman

Franz Schubert

1. God has num-bered in the sky   All the stars that shine on high;
2. He re-mem-bers night and day   Ev -'ry child at work or play;

Worlds so great and spar-rows small; God is watch-ing o - ver all.
He will teach you what to do;   God is watch-ing o - ver you.

Folks We Like to Know

In the early, shivery dark
Of wintertime I wake
And hear the klinkey-klank
That our milk bottles make.[1]

Rhoda W. Bacmeister

Jiggity Jog

After a nursery rhyme   L. B. P.

1. Jig - gi - ty jog, jig - gi - ty jog,
2. Jig - gi - ty jog, jig - gi - ty jog,

I am the milk - man's horse · named Nogg,
O - ver the hills · and o - ver the bog,

Jig - gi - ty - jog, jig - gi - ty - jog,
Jig - gi - ty - jog, jig - gi - ty - jog,

Bring - ing your milk · · through all · this fog.
Safe - ly back home · comes Nog - gi - ty Nogg.

[1]From *Stories to Begin On*, by Rhoda W. Bacmeister, published and copyrighted 1940 by E. P. Dutton & Co., Inc., New York.

The Ice-Cream Man

Rachel Field

Charles J. Cromwell

When sum-mer's in the cit - y, And brick's a blaze of heat,

The Ice-cream Man with his lit - tle cart Goes trun-dling down the street.

Be - neath his round um-brel - la, Oh, what a joy - ful sight,

To see him fill the cones with rounds Of cool - ing brown or white.

The Scissor-Man

Madeline Nightingale

Francis Hilliard

Sing a song of Scis-sor-men, "Mend a brok-en plate,

Bring your knives and gar-den shears, I'll do them while you wait.

Buzz - a - wuzz! Buzz - a - wuzz! Fast the wheel or slow,

Tick - er tack - er! Tick - er tack! Riv - ets in a row."

The Postman

Meadowbrook School Children

Post-man, Post-man, you're on your way. Do you have a let-ter for me to-day?

Post-man, Post-man, you walk, walk, walk. Do you ev - er talk, talk, talk?

Pretty Girls and the Shoemaker

Translated by
Cecil Cowdrey

Argentine Folk Song

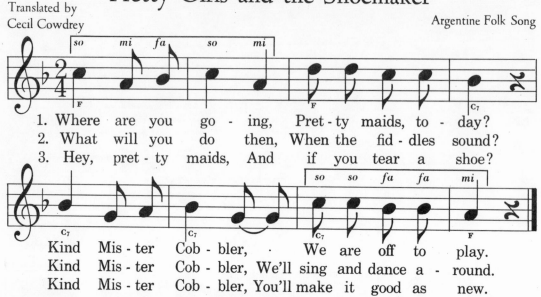

so   mi   fa   so   mi

1. Where are you go - ing, Pret - ty maids, to - day?
2. What will you do then, When the fid - dles sound?
3. Hey, pret - ty maids, And if you tear a shoe?

so   so   fa   fa   mi

Kind Mis - ter Cob - bler, · We are off to play.
Kind Mis - ter Cob - bler, We'll sing and dance a - round.
Kind Mis - ter Cob - bler, You'll make it good as new.

The Street Organ

Yugoslavian Folk Tune

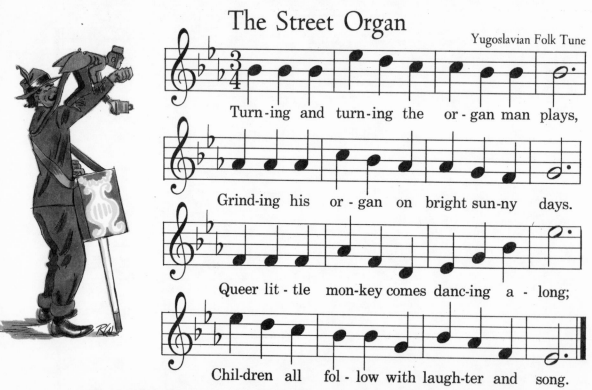

Turn - ing and turn - ing the or - gan man plays,

Grind - ing his or - gan on bright sun - ny days.

Queer lit - tle mon - key comes danc - ing a - long;

Chil - dren all fol - low with laugh - ter and song.

Listen to "Run, Run" (Hurdy-gurdy tune) from *Memories of Childhood*, Pinto.
(Victor Listening Album One.)

66

The Fireman

C. J. C.

Charles J. Cromwell

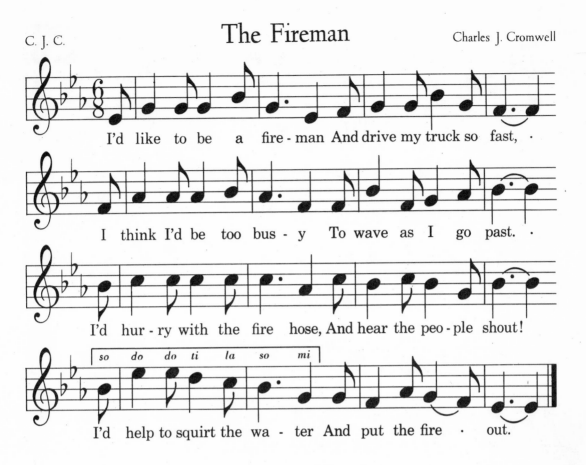

I'd like to be a fire-man And drive my truck so fast,

I think I'd be too bus-y To wave as I go past.

I'd hur-ry with the fire hose, And hear the peo-ple shout!

so do do ti la so mi

I'd help to squirt the wa-ter And put the fire out.

The Funny Old Clown

Meadowbrook School Children

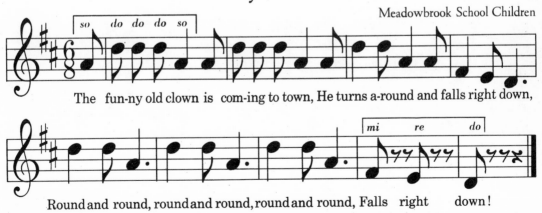

so do do do so

The fun-ny old clown is com-ing to town, He turns a-round and falls right down,

mi re do

Round and round, round and round, round and round, Falls right down!

Listen to "Clowns" from *Midsummer-Night's Dream*, Mendelssohn. (Victor Rhythm Album One.)

Birthdays

My Birthday

C. J. C.

Charles J. Cromwell

so do so do do mi do

Oh, I'm so hap-py to-day! · Hoo-ray, hoo-ray, hoo-ray! ·

Oh, I'm so hap-py to-day! · My birth-day is to-day! ·

Happy Birthday

German Folk Tune

do mi so so

Hap-py Birth-day, Hap-py Birth-day, Hap-py Birth-day, to you.

Hap-py Birth-day, Hap-py Birth-day, Hap-py Birth-day to you.

do do ti la ti do

Hap-py Birth-day Hap-py Birth-day, Hap-py Birth-day to you.

68

Birthdays Are Such Jolly Times

A. F.

Arthur Findley

Oh, birth-days are such jol - ly times With pres-ents and good wish-es,

And can-dle cake with frost-ing on And ice-cream heaped in dish-es.

Oh, birth-days are such jol - ly times With pic - nic trips to go on,

And spanks if they can catch me, With a whop-ping one to grow on.

Halloween

A fairy seed I planted,
So dry and white and old;
There sprang a vine enchanted,
With magic flowers of gold.

I watched it, I tended it,
And truly, by and by,
It bore a jack-o'-lantern,
And a great Thanksgiving pie.

Halloween Is Coming

Verna Meade Surer

1. Hal-low-een is com-ing, when we'll be
   Dressed in fun-ny clothes and then we'll see
   Pump-kins in the win-dows, shin-ing bright.
   Oh, we'll have a good time on Hal-low-een night.

2. Bob-bing for the ap-ples, oh, what fun,
   Then we'll go a-call-ing on the run.
   Witch-es with their broom-sticks, such a sight!
   Yes, we'll have a good time on Hal-low-een night.

70

Halloween

M. R.

Mysteriously

Moiselle Renstrom

la   ti   do   re   mi   fa   mi

1. Oo . . . . . . 'Tis the night of Hal-low-een;
2. Oo . . . . . . Witch-es, black cats, gob-lins too;

Oo . . . . . . When such fun-ny things are seen.
Oo . . . . . . All will try to fright-en you.

Oo . . . Oo . . Boo!
Oo . . . Oo . . Boo!

Jack-O'-Lantern

Susanna Myers

Lettish Folk Tune

la   ti   do   re   mi   do   ti   la

1. Jack-o'-lan-tern burns his can-dle Bright through the wind-y night;
2. Owls up-on the wav-ing tree-tops Hoot through the wind-y night;

Witch-es   on their broom-sticks ride By the Jack-o'-lan-tern light.
Brown-ies dance on Hal-low-een By the Jack-o'-lan-tern light.

71

What a Surprise

F. H.

Francis Hilliard

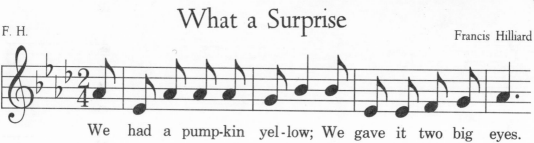

We had a pump-kin yel-low; We gave it two big eyes.

We cut a round and ti - ny nose, A fun-ny mouth that smiles.

Now we'll hide be - hind the hedge, And wait un - til it's dark;

Then when Dad-dy comes a-long, Up we jump, "Boo," we'll shout, What a sur - prise!

Boo!

Louise Sheldon

L. S.

Boo! Boo! I'll scare you On this Hal-low-een night!

Boo! Boo! Scare me too On this Hal-low-een night! Boo!

The Wind Is Howling

Gretchen E. Van Roy

G. E. V. R.

Mysteriously

The wind is howl-ing through the night. Oo · · · · · ·

And witch-es ride on broom-sticks light. Oo · · · · · ·

Then all the fun-ny girls and boys in scar-y clothes with scar-y noise

Will fright-en all the folks in sight. Oo · · · · · · Boo!

Listen to "Gnomes," Reinhold. (Victor Rhythm Album One.)

Thanksgiving

The winds and raindrops help us to remember
That this is Thanksgiving month, jolly November.

Wilhelmina Smith

Over the River and Through the Wood

Lydia Maria Child   Composer Unknown

1. O - ver the riv - er and through the wood,
2. O - ver the riv - er and through the wood,

To grand - fa - ther's house we go;
And straight through the barn - yard gate.

The horse knows the way to car - ry the sleigh,
We seem to go ex - treme - ly slow,

Through the white and drift - ed snow.
It is so hard to wait!

74

O - ver the riv - er and through the wood,
O - ver the riv - er and through the wood,

Oh, how · the wind does blow! ·
Now grand-moth-er's cap I spy! ·

It stings · the toes, And · bites the nose,
Hur - rah for the fun! Is the pud-ding done?

As o - ver the ground we go. · ·
Hur - rah for the pump - kin pie! ·

Prayer

Marian Major

M. M.

Thank You for the world so sweet, Thank You for the food we eat.

so do do fa mi re do

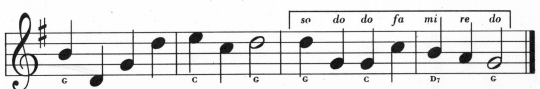

Thank You for the birds that sing, Thank You, God, for ev - 'ry-thing.

75

He's a Big Fat Turkey

He's a big fat tur-key on grand-pa's farm Who thinks he's ver-y gay.

He spreads his tail in-to a great big fan And struts a-round all day.

You should hear him gob-ble at the girls and boys.

He thinks he's sing-ing when he makes that noise.

He'll sing his song a dif-f'rent way Up-on Thanks-giv-ing Day.

Christmas

I'm counting each day on my fingers and thumbs
The weeks that must pass before Santa Claus comes.

The Little Bells

Old Round

The lit-tle bells of Christ-mas ring, Ding, ding, ding, dong, ding.

Play bells.

Now It's Christmas Time

Paraphrased

Swedish Folk Song

Now it's Christ-mas time, oh, now it's Christ-mas time,

And Christ-mas time will last till New Year.

Now it's Christ-mas time, oh, now it's Christ-mas time,

The time for hap-pi-ness and good cheer.

77

Up on the House-Top

Traditional

1. Up on the house-top the rein-deer pause,
2. First comes the stock-ing of lit-tle Nell;
3. Look in the stock-ing of lit-tle Bill;

Out jumps good old · San-ta Claus;
Oh, dear San-ta, · fill it well;
Oh, just see what a glo-rious fill!

Down through the chim-ney with lots of toys,
Give her a doll-y that laughs and cries,
Here is a ham-mer and lots of tacks,

All for the lit-tle ones'· Christ-mas joys.
One that can o - pen and shut its eyes.
Whis-tle and ball · and a whip that cracks.

CHORUS

Ho, ho, ho! who would-n't go!

Ho, ho, ho! who would-n't go!

78

Up on the house-top, click, click, click,

Tone block.

Down through the chim-ney with good Saint Nick.

Old Santa's Coming

Johannes Brahms

1. Jing - a - ling - a - ling,   Old   San - ta's   com - ing,
2. Jing - a - ling - a - ling,   I   hear   him   com - ing,

Play sleigh bells

Jing - a - ling - a - ling,   What   brings   him   here?
Jing - a - ling - a - ling,   What   else   has   he?

do ti do ti do

Jing - a - ling - a - ling,   Nice   sug - ar   can - dy,
Jing - a - ling - a - ling,   Such   pret - ty   play - things,

so fa mi re do

Jing - a - ling - a - ling,   For   me, his lit - tle dear.
Jing - a - ling - a - ling,   A   bun - dle full for me.

A Carol

E. D. B.

Ella Des Brisay

so so la so mi do

The birds sing their car-ols so love-ly and sweet,

The an - i-mals gath-er, the wee one to greet,

The chil-dren are bring-ing their gifts to the stall,

They've all come to wor-ship the Ba - by so small

Away in a Manger

Martin Luther

so so fa mi mi re do do ti la so

1. A - way in a man - ger, no crib for His bed,
2. The cat - tle are low - ing, the Ba - by a - wakes,

The lit - tle Lord Je - sus laid down His sweet head.
The lit - tle Lord Je - sus no cry - ing He makes.

The stars in the sky · looked down where He lay.
I love Thee, Lord Je - sus! Look down from the sky.

The lit - tle Lord Je - sus a - sleep in the hay.
And stay by my cra - dle till morn - ing is nigh.

I'm a Little Christmas Tree

Ella Elizabeth Preston

John Langland

I'm a lit-tle Christ-mas tree, Glit-ter-ing, glit-ter-ing mer-ri - ly,

A star at my head and gifts at my feet,

On all of my branch-es can-dy canes sweet.

Listen to "March of the Gnomes" from *Christmas Tree Suite*, Rebikoff. (Victor Listening Album Three.)

81

I Wish You a Merry Christmas

Cornish Folk Tune

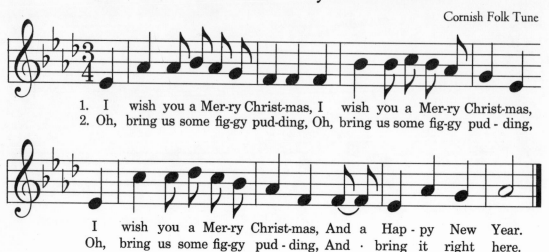

1. I wish you a Mer-ry Christ-mas, I wish you a Mer-ry Christ-mas,
2. Oh, bring us some fig-gy pud-ding, Oh, bring us some fig-gy pud - ding,

I wish you a Mer-ry Christ-mas, And a Hap - py New Year.
Oh, bring us some fig-gy pud - ding, And · bring it right here.

Hear the Christmas Bells

Kansas City School Children

Hear the Christ-mas bells   Ring -ing ev - 'ry - where.

Bing!   Bong!   Bing!   Bong!   Sings the big · bell.

Ding, dong, ding, dong, ding, dong, ding, dong, Sings the lit - tle bell.

Ting-a-ling-a, ting-a-ling-a, ting-a-ling-a, ting-a-ling-a, Sings the ba - by bell.

How Lovely Are the Messengers (From "St. Paul")

Romans, V: 15, 16

Felix Mendelssohn-Bartholdy

How love-ly are the mes-sen-gers that preach us the gos-pel of peace;

How love-ly are the mes-sen-gers that preach us the gos-pel of peace.

Silent Night

Joseph Mohr

Franz Gruber

Si - lent night, Ho - ly night! All is calm, all is bright

Round yon Vir - gin Moth-er and Child.

Ho - ly In - fant so ten-der and mild,

Sleep in heav-en-ly peace, Sleep in heav-en-ly peace.

83

We Three Kings of Orient Are

J. H. H.

John H. Hopkins

do do do so do la do

Star of won-der, star of might, Star with roy-al beau-ty bright,

rit.

West-ward lead-ing, still pro-ceed-ing, Guide us to the per-fect light.

Long Ago

Author Unknown

Lilla Belle Pitts

so so fa mi re do

F C7 C7 dm gm C7 F

1. Winds through the ol-ive trees, · Soft-ly did blow, ·
2. Sheep on the hill-side lay, · Whit-er than snow, ·
3. Then from the hap-py sky, · An-gels bent low ·
4. For in a man-ger bed · Cra-dled, we know ·

C dm dm gm C7 F

Round · lit-tle Beth-le-hem, Long, long a-go.
Shep-herds were watch-ing them, Long, long a-go.
Sing-ing their songs of joy, Long, long a-go.
Christ · came to Beth-le-hem, Long, long a-go.

84

O Come, All Ye Faithful (Adeste Fideles)

F. Oakeley

Old Latin

O come, all ye faith-ful, Joy-ful and tri-um-phant,

O come ye, O come ye to Beth - le - hem;

Come and be-hold Him, Born the King of An - gels;

O come, let us a - dore Him, O come, let us a - dore Him,

O come, let us a - dore Him, · Christ, · the Lord.

Washington's and Lincoln's Birthdays

I pledge allegiance to the flag of the United States of America and to the Republic for which it stands; one nation under God, indivisible, with liberty and justice for all.

America

Samuel Francis Smith

Traditional

1. My coun-try, 'tis of thee, Sweet land of lib-er-ty, Of thee I sing.
2. Our fa-thers' God to Thee, Au-thor of lib-er-ty, To Thee we sing.

Land where my fa-thers died! Land of the Pil-grims' pride!
Long may our land be bright With free-dom's ho-ly light;

From ev-'ry moun-tain side, Let free-dom ring!
Pro-tect us by Thy might, Great God our king!

Yankee Doodle

Traditional

1. Fath'r and I went down to camp, A-long with Cap-tain Good-win,
2. There was Cap-tain Wash-ing-ton, Up-on a slap-ping stal-lion,

And there we saw the men and boys, As thick as hast-y pud-ding.
A-giv-ing or-ders to his men; I guess there was a mil-lion.

la ti la so la ti do

Yan-kee Doo-dle keep it up, Yan-kee Doo-dle dan-dy,

Mind the mu-sic and the step, And with the girls be hand-y.

Battle Hymn of the Republic

Julia Ward Howe

William Steffe

Glo-ry, glo-ry, hal-le-lu-jah! Glo-ry, glo-ry, hal-le-lu-jah!

do re re do ti do

Glo-ry, glo-ry, hal-le-lu-jah! His truth is march-ing on.

87

The Star-Spangled Banner

Francis Scott Key   John Stafford Smith

Oh, · say! can you see, by the dawn's ear - ly light,

What so proud - ly we hailed at the twi-light's last gleam-ing,

Whose broad stripes and bright stars, through the per - i - lous fight

O'er the ram-parts we watched were so gal - lant - ly stream-ing?

And the rock - ets' red glare, the bombs burst-ing in air,

Gave proof through the night that our flag was still there.

Oh, say does that · Star-span-gled Ban - ner · yet · wave ·

O'er the land · of the free and the home of the brave?

There Are Many Flags in Many Lands

M H. Howliston

Composer Unknown

There are man-y flags in man-y lands, There are flags of ev-'ry hue;

But there is no flag how ev-er grand, Like our own Red, White and Blue.

CHORUS

Then hur-rah for the flag, Our coun-try's flag, Its stripes and white stars, too;

There is no flag in an-y land Like our own Red, White and Blue.

America the Beautiful

Katharine Lee Bates

Samuel A. Ward

O beau-ti-ful for spa-cious skies, For am-ber waves of grain,

For pur-ple moun-tain maj-es-ties A-bove the fruit-ed plain!

A-mer-i-ca! A-mer-i-ca! God shed His grace on thee,

And crown thy good with broth-er-hood, From sea to shin-ing sea!

Valentine's Day

As sure as the vine
Grows 'round the stump
You are my darling sugar lump.

When You Send a Valentine

Mildred J. Hill

Louella Garrett

When you send a val - en - tine, That's the time for fun.

Push it un - der-neath the door, Ring the bell and run, run, run, run!

Ring the bell and run!

Father's Valentine

Dorothy Langley

Paul Forde

I gave fa - ther a val - en - tine,

It had his name in a heart with mine,

It had my name in a heart with his,

And a sil - ver cu - pid blow-ing a kiss.

He was sur-prised with the cu - pid part,

so fa mi re re do

But he said he was used to my name in his heart.

Easter

There's a Little Bunny

Ellen Underhill Bishop

mi mi mi mi so so

There's a lit-tle bun-ny sit-ting on a hill;

With his ears stand-ing up, he sits ver-y still.

Will he come to your house, will he come to mine?

do la la so so fa mi re do

Hop o-ver, Bun-ny, at East-er time.

Easter Time

Ellen Underhill Bishop

mi   mi   so

Eas-er time, East-er time, Flow-ers bloom at East-er time.

Church bells ring, chil-dren sing, Hap-py, hap-py East-er time.

The Easter Egg

Christine Turner Curtis

Italian Children's Song

re   re   re   do   do

Hail, hap-py East-er, my fat white hen is sing-ing.

She'll lay an egg for break-fast, while all the bells are ring-ing,

But see my old red roost-er, he's ver-y lean and bon-y,

He needs some mac-a-ro-ni.

94

ABOUT SONGS
OF THE WORLD

The stars were shouting in heaven,
The sun was chasing the moon:
The game was the same as the children's,
They danced to the selfsame tune.

A. E.

Good Morning, Sky!

Fannie R. Buchanan

John Langland

Good morn-ing, sky! Good morn-ing, sun! Good morn-ing, lit-tle winds that run!

Good morn-ing, birds! Good morn-ing, trees, And creep-ing grass, and brown-ie bees!

How did you find out it was day? Who told you night had gone a-way?

I'm wide a-wake; I'm up now, too. I'll be right out to play with you!

Wind and Weather

I heard the wind call out and say:
"Get up, my dear, it is today!"

Rachel Field

The Wind

N. B. E.

Nora Belle Emerson

High up o-ver the tree-tops The wind sings a song,

Wooooooooooo, woooooooooo, What a pret-ty song,

Wooooooooooo, woooooooooo, Such a pret-ty song.

97

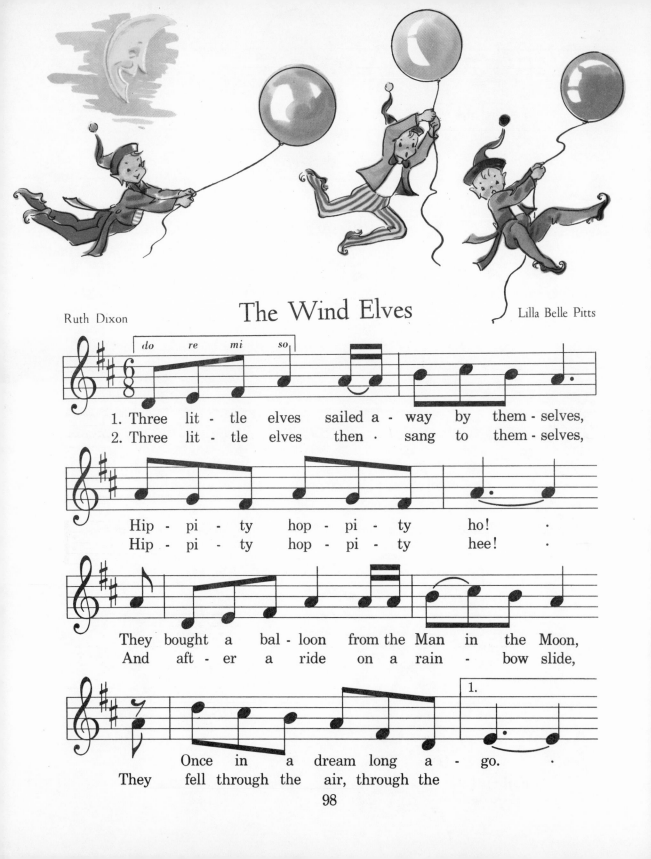

The Wind Elves

Ruth Dixon

Lilla Belle Pitts

do re mi so

1. Three lit - tle elves sailed a - way by them - selves,
2. Three lit - tle elves then · sang to them - selves,

Hip - pi - ty hop - pi - ty ho! ·
Hip - pi - ty hop - pi - ty hee! ·

They bought a bal - loon from the Man in the Moon,
And aft - er a ride on a rain - bow slide,

Once in a dream long a - go. ·
They fell through the air, through the

98

And out in the wind they wig - gled and spinned,

A - round and a - round in a row.

air, *Whee!* And land - ed ker - flop on the tip - pi - ty top

Of their fa - vor - ite rock - a - by tree.

In my bed all safe and warm
I like to listen to the storm.
The thunder rumbles loud and grand—
The rain goes splash and whisper; and
The lightning is so sharp and bright
It sticks its fingers through the night.[1]

Dorothy Aldis

Nursery Rhyme

A Goblin Lives in Our House

Paul Forde

A gob-lin lives in our house, in our house, in our · house,

A gob-lin lives in our house, all the year · round. ·

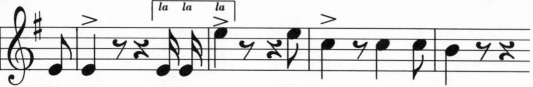

He bumps. And he jumps. He thumps And he stumps,

He knocks And he rocks, And he rat-tles at the locks.

[1]From *Everything and Anything*, by Dorothy Aldis. Copyright, 1925, 1926, 1927, by Dorothy Aldis. Courtesy of G. P. Putnam's Sons.

Comes the Rain

I want to go dancing
With the rain,
Off through the garden
Over the plain.

James S. Tippett

On a Rainy Day

Josephine Royle

John P. Sacco

Lightly

mi   do   so so so so so

1. Rain,   rain,   fall-ing all a-round, Rain, rain, fall-ing on the ground;
2. One,   two, now we turn a-round, Three, four, stamp up-on the ground;

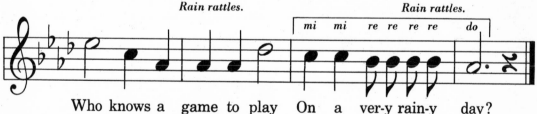

Rain rattles.   *Rain rattles.*

mi   mi   re re re re   do

Who knows a   game to play   On   a   ver-y rain-y   day?
We   know a   game to play   On   a   ver-y rain-y   day.

Rain rattles.

3. Five, six, tap your rhythm stick,
   Seven, eight, click, click, click, click, click;
   We know a game to play
   On a very rainy day.

4. Nine, ten, make your cymbals clang,
   'Leven, twelve, let your drums go bang;
   We know a game to play
   On a very rainy day.

101

Rain in the Night

Amelia Josephine Burr

Lydia Elwood

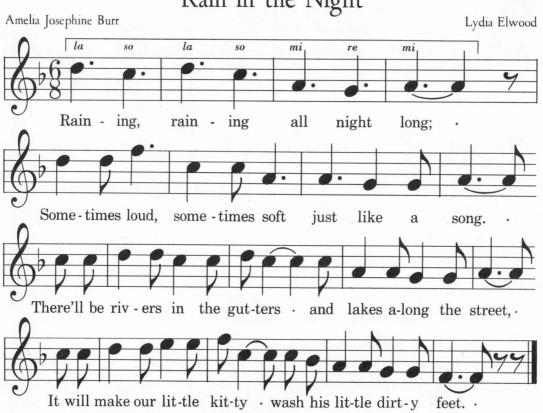

la   so   la   so   mi   re   mi

Rain - ing, rain - ing all night long; ·

Some - times loud, some - times soft just like a song. ·

There'll be riv - ers in the gut - ters · and lakes a-long the street, ·

It will make our lit - tle kit - ty · wash his lit - tle dirt - y feet. ·

Drops of Water

E. C. Brewer

Unknown

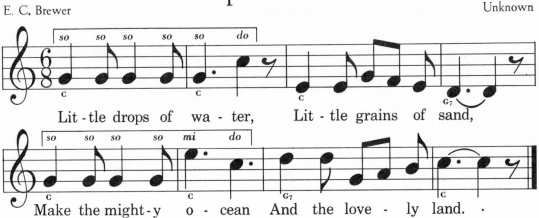

Lit -tle drops of wa - ter, Lit - tle grains of sand,

Make the might-y o - cean And the love - ly land.

Hear the Rain

L. B. P.

L. B. P.

Pit - ter pat - ter, pit - ter pat - ter, hear the rain,

Rain rattles.
Rhythm sticks, lightly tapped.

Pit - ter pat - ter, pit - ter pat - ter on the pane.

Pit - ter pat - ter, pit - ter pat - ter com - ing down,

slower

Drip - ping, drip - ping on the town.

The Happy River

L. B. P.

French Folk Tune

Hear the hap-py riv-er sing-ing, sing-ing,
1 2 3 4 5 3 5 3 5 3,
Do re mi fa so mi so mi so mi,

Hear the hap-py riv-er sing-ing as it flows.
1 2 3 4 5 3 5 4 3 2 1.
Do re mi fa so mi so fa mi re do.

River Song

K. S. B.

Katherine Smith Bolt

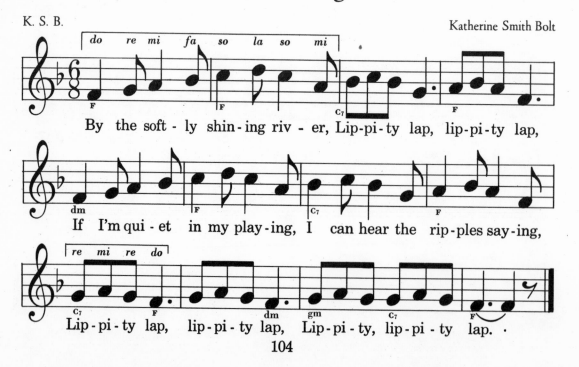

do re mi fa so la so mi

By the soft-ly shin-ing riv-er, Lip-pi-ty lap, lip-pi-ty lap,

If I'm qui-et in my play-ing, I can hear the rip-ples say-ing,

re mi re do

Lip-pi-ty lap, lip-pi-ty lap, Lip-pi-ty, lip-pi-ty lap.

Row, Row, Row Your Boat

E. O. Lyte

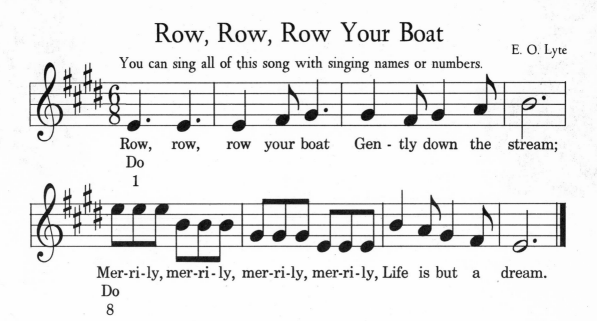

You can sing all of this song with singing names or numbers.

Row, row, row your boat Gen-tly down the stream;
Do
1

Mer-ri-ly, mer-ri-ly, mer-ri-ly, mer-ri-ly, Life is but a dream.
Do
8

When I Travel

Translated

German Children's Song

When I trav-el on the sea, Where the lit-tle gold-fish play,

Then I sing so mer-ri-ly, While I sail my boat so gay.

so mi so mi so mi do

Sing, sing, sing so mer-ri-ly,

The gold-fish, the gold-fish, they fol-low me.

Sun, Moon, and Stars

High overhead and all moving about,
There were thousands of millions of stars!

R. L. S.

Twinkle, Twinkle, Little Star

Traditional

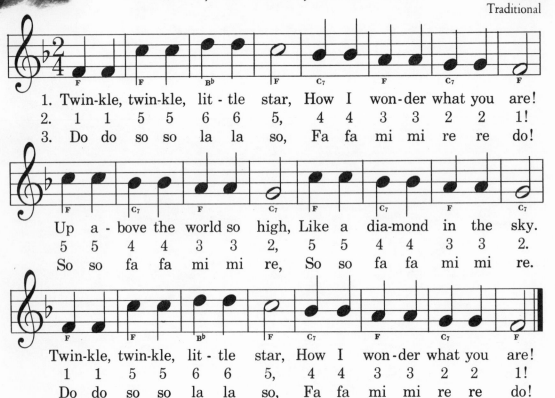

1. Twin-kle, twin-kle, lit - tle star, How I won-der what you are!
2. 1   1   5   5   6   6   5,   4   4   3   3   2   2   1!
3. Do   do   so   so   la   la   so,   Fa   fa   mi   mi   re   re   do!

Up a - bove the world so high, Like a dia-mond in the sky.
5   5   4   4   3   3   2,   5   5   4   4   3   3   2.
So   so   fa   fa   mi   mi   re,   So   so   fa   fa   mi   mi   re.

Twin-kle, twin-kle, lit - tle star, How I won-der what you are!
1   1   5   5   6   6   5,   4   4   3   3   2   2   1!
Do   do   so   so   la   la   so,   Fa   fa   mi   mi   re   re   do!

Playing in the Sun

Louise Ayres Garnett   French Folk Tune

do   so   so   so   la   so   fa   mi

Take my hand, let us hur-ry out, Out in the sun.

106

First we'll go whirl-ing in a spin, Like tops when spin-ning they be-gin;

Then we'll go run-ning all a-bout; Fun, oh, what fun!

The Man in the Moon

E. B.

Edna Blethen

Not too slowly

The man in the moon is as round as can be,

As he wrin-kles and twin-kles his eyes at me;

And here on my pil-low I wish him good night,

As he wrin-kles and twin-kles his eyes so bright.

107

I will sing to the trees,
I will sing to the stars in the sky.

Sara Teasdale

Stars

Rhoda W. Bacmeister [1]   Velma Hanlin

1. Bright · stars, light stars, Shin - ing - in - the - night stars,
2. Yel - low stars, red stars, Shine-when-I'm - in - bed stars,

Lit - tle twin - kly, win - kly stars, Deep in the sky.
Oh, how man - y blin - ky stars, Far, far a - way.

Up in the Deep, Dark Sky

L. B. P.   French XVIII Century

Far up in the deep, · dark sky, ·

The white moon goes sail - ing, goes sail - ing by;

[1] From *Stories to Begin On*, by Rhoda W. Bacmeister, published and copyrighted 1940
by E. P. Dutton & Co., Inc., New York.

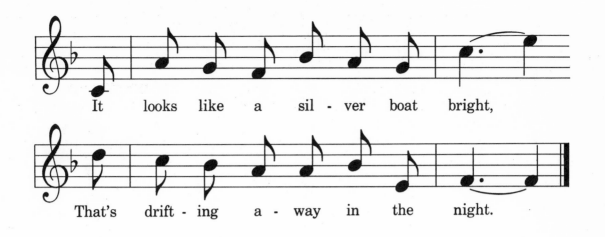

It looks like a sil - ver boat bright,

That's drift - ing a - way in the night.

The Moon-Cradle's Rocking

Padraic Colum

Paul Forde

With gentle rocking motion

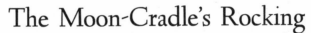

The moon-cra-dle's rock-ing and rock - ing,

Where a cloud and a cloud · goes by: ·

Si - lent - ly rock-ing and rock - ing,

The moon-cra-dle out in the sky. ·

The Circling Seasons

Autumn

We hail the merry autumn days,
When leaves are turning red;
Because they're far more beautiful
Than any one has said.

Charles Dickens

Shake the Apple Tree

Carl Reinecke

Hap-py lit - tle John - nie, Pol-ly, come with me;

Come in - to the gar - den, Shake the ap - ple tree;

I will shake the big ones, You will shake the small;

When we've filled our bas - ket Home we'll take them all.

Hap-py lit - tle John - nie, Shake the ap - ple tree.

110

Round the Pear Tree

Lois Lenski

Danish Folk Tune

do so so re so so

1. Here we go · tip-py toe, Danc-ing round the pear tree;
2. Branch-es low, here we go Climb-ing up the pear tree;

Pears may fall, catch them all. Did-dle, dump-ty, dai - rie!
Pears are sweet, good to eat. Did-dle, dump-ty, dai - rie!

Autumn

A. Arthur Knipe

James Seton

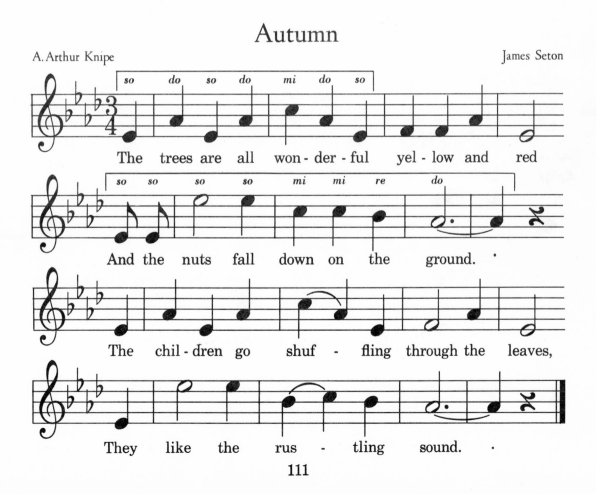

so do so do mi do so

The trees are all won - der - ful yel - low and red

so so so so mi mi re do

And the nuts fall down on the ground. ·

The chil - dren go shuf - fling through the leaves,

They like the rus - tling sound. ·

Jack Frost

Peggy Berron

Barry S. Brinsmaid

do   do

1. Jack Frost,   Jack Frost came up-on   a   win-try night;
2. Jack Frost,   Jack Frost paint-ed   on   the   win-dow pane;
3. Jack Frost,   Jack Frost, rid-ing   on   a   white snow-flake.

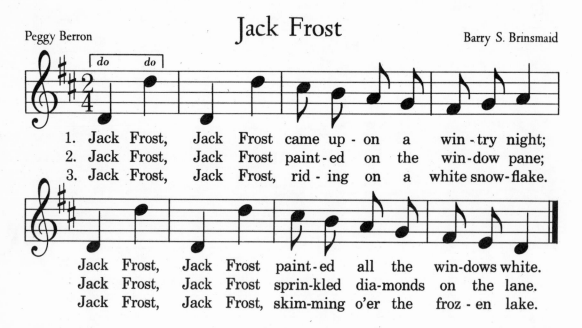

Jack Frost,   Jack Frost paint-ed   all   the   win-dows white.
Jack Frost,   Jack Frost sprin-kled   dia-monds   on   the lane.
Jack Frost,   Jack Frost, skim-ming o'er the   froz-en   lake.

Autumn Leaves

P. K. F.

Pauline K. Fisher

See   the love-ly   au-tumn leaves of   red and gold and   brown.

Gen-tly float-ing   on the breeze, then rest-ing on   the   ground.

It's Fun to Pick Potatoes

Children's Song

1. It's fun to pick po - ta - toes, It's fun to pick the corn. ·
2. It's fun to pick the pump-kins, It's fun to pick the squash, ·

It's fun to pick to - ma-toes On an ear - ly frost-y morn. ·
And now that we have picked them all, We must go in and wash. ·

Lavender's Blue

Old English Singing Game

1. Lav - en - der's blue, dil - ly, dil - ly, Lav - en - der's green.
2. Call up your men, dil - ly, dil - ly, Set them to work;
3. Some to make hay, dil - ly, dil - ly, Some to cut corn,

When I am king, dil - ly, dil - ly, You shall be queen.
Some to the plow, dil - ly, dil - ly, Some to the cart.
While you and I, dil - ly, dil - ly, Keep our - selves warm.

Winter

Oh! the snow, the beautiful snow,
Filling the sky and the earth below;
Over the house tops, over the street,
Over the heads of the people you meet;
    Dancing,
        Flirting,
            Skimming along,
Beautiful snow! it can do nothing wrong.

J. W. Watson

The Cat Is in the Snow

Translated

German Children's Song

1. Oh, oh, oh! The cat is in the snow.
2. Oh, oh, oh! The cat was in the snow.

When back she comes, oh, what a sight,
Now by the fire she licks her paws

She's wear - ing boots of snow - y white,
And then she sharp - ens up her claws,

Oh, jim - i - nee, oh, jim - i - no! Now where will kit - ty go?
Oh, jim - i - nee, oh, jim - i - no! Our cat was in the snow!

Two Winds

Mary Louise Allen

Marian Deere

In sum-mer the wind is soft and slow,

Woo - oo - oo, I hear him go,

so do re mi fa so la so

But when he's bring - ing win - ter snow,

la ti do ti la so fa mi re do

WOO-OO-OO - OO-OO, I hear · him blow.

Coasting

L. S.

Louise Sheldon

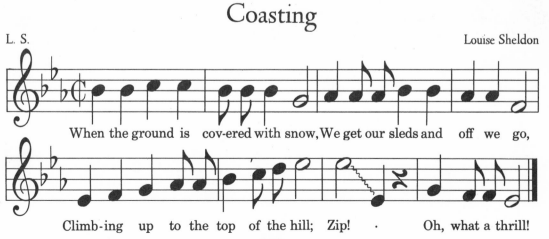

When the ground is cov-ered with snow, We get our sleds and off we go,

Climb-ing up to the top of the hill; Zip! · Oh, what a thrill!

It's Snowing

A. W.

Angela Wiechard

mi mi re re do so

I'm so glad it's snow-ing, Tra la la la la.

I'll shov-el the snow in the front yard, Shov-el the snow in the back yard.

so fa mi re do

I'm so glad it's snow-ing, Tra la la la la.

The Snowflakes

E. S. D.

Esther S. Duncan

1. The snow is fly - ing all the night long On ti - ny si - lent wings.
2. "I'll cov - er all the world to-night, I'll keep it safe from harm,

It falls on hill, on tree and ground And soft - ly sings.
I'll wrap it in a love - ly coat And keep it warm."

I slip and I slide
On the slippery ice;
I skid and I glide,—
Oh, isn't it nice
To lie on your tummy
And slither and skim
On the slick crust of snow
Where you skid as you swim?[1]

Rhoda W. Bacmeister

Skating

W. H.

Walter Howland

do   re   mi   do

Skat - ing,   skat - ing, Skat-ing to left and to   right.

Pretend to skate with your hands.

Slid - ing,   glid - ing, Glid-ing to left and to   right.

How many of you can play this piece on the piano with both hands?

[1]Taken from *Stories to Begin On*, by Rhoda W. Bacmeister, published and copyrighted 1940 by E. P. Dutton & Co., Inc., New York.

Spring

I'm happy and merry:
I sing again
Because today
It is Spring again.

Ilo Orleans

It's Spring

Nancy Byrd Turner   John Langland

1. Oh hur-ry, gath-er daf-fo-dils!
2. Oh hur-ry, fetch your bat and ball,

They're scat-tered o-ver all the hills As thick as an-y-thing!
Put on your old-est shoes of all, And cap and ev-'ry-thing.

The lit-tle buds un-fold a-gain, In buff and white and gold a-gain.
It's turn-ing fine and hot a-gain, The boys are in the lot a-gain.

It's spring, spring, spring! · It's spring, spring, spring! ·
It's spring, spring, spring! · It's spring, spring, spring! ·

Listen to "The Swiss Maid," Traditional. (Victor Rhythm Album Five.)

There Came to My Window

English

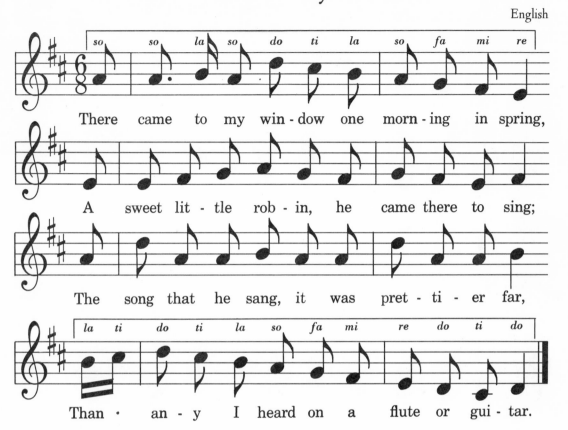

so   so   la   so   do   ti   la   so   fa   mi   re

There came to my win-dow one morn-ing in spring,

A sweet lit-tle rob-in, he came there to sing;

The song that he sang, it was pret-ti-er far,

la   ti   do   ti   la   so   fa   mi   re   do   ti   do

Than · an-y I heard on a flute or gui-tar.

Fun in Our Garden

Kansas City School Children

It's fun to work in our gar-den, It's fun to weed and hoe, ·

faster
so   la   la   ti   ti   do

It's fun to plant the ti-ny seeds, It's fun to watch them grow. ·

Daffodils

Mary Brockwell

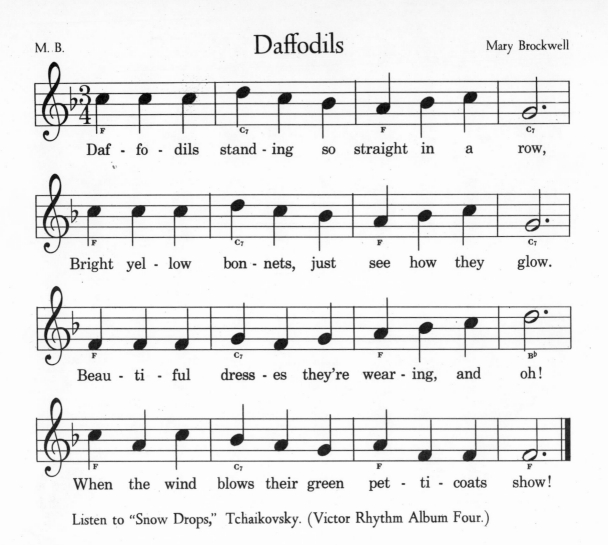

Daf - fo - dils stand - ing so straight in a row,

Bright yel - low bon - nets, just see how they glow.

Beau - ti - ful dress - es they're wear - ing, and oh!

When the wind blows their green pet - ti - coats show!

Listen to "Snow Drops," Tchaikovsky. (Victor Rhythm Album Four.)

ABOUT CREATURES GREAT AND SMALL

All things bright and beautiful,
All creatures great and small,
All things wise and wonderful,
The Lord God made them all.

Cecil Frances Alexander

121

Butterflies, Bugs,
and Other Things

Fuzzy wuzzy, creepy crawly
Caterpillar funny,
You will be a butterfly
When the days are sunny.

Winging, flinging, dancing, springing,
Butterfly so yellow,
You were once a caterpillar,
Wiggly, wiggly fellow.

Lillian Schulz

Butterfly

Nursery Rhyme

French Folk Tune

"But - ter - fly, where are you go - ing?

But - ter - fly, where do you go?"

"Out in the bright sun-shine, there do I go,

so la ti do so | *so fa mi re do*

For where there are flow'rs, I al-ways will go."

Listen to "Etude in G Flat Major" (Butterfly), Chopin. (Victor Listening Album Five.)

Bees and Frogs

Takeru Iijima

1. Hon - ey bees are buzz - ing round the gar - den hive, ·
2. By the lit - tle pool where all the lil - ies grow, ·

All the chil-dren count them, One, two, three, four, five. ·
Ti - ny frogs are sit - ting In a nice neat row. ·

Listen to "The Bee," Schubert. (Victor Listening Album Three.)

The Firefly

Nadine Bensley

N. B.

so la so la so do ti la so

Pret-ty lit-tle fire - fly in the night,

When the sky is dark you have a light.

Fly-ing here and there you do not mind

Be-cause you have a tail-light on be - hind.

123

Chicchirichi[1]

Translated

Italian Children's Song

mi mi mi do

"Chic-chi-ri-chi, we're three lit-tle ants."

"Cuc-cu-ru-cu,[2] where are you go-ing?"

"Chic-chi-ri-chi, to take a bath."

"Cuc-cu-ru-cu, when will you come back?"

"Chic-chi-ri-chi, we'll come this eve-ning."

"Cuc-cu-ru-cu, we'll ask you to sup-per."

Pronounced: [1] kee-kee-ree-kee [2] coo-coo-roo-coo.

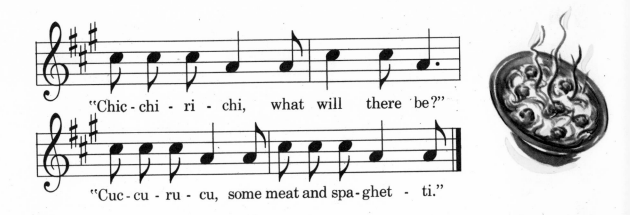

"Chic - chi - ri - chi,   what will   there be?"

"Cuc - cu - ru - cu, some meat and spa - ghet - ti."

Mr. Mosquito

Katherine Smith Bolt

Richard H. Bolt

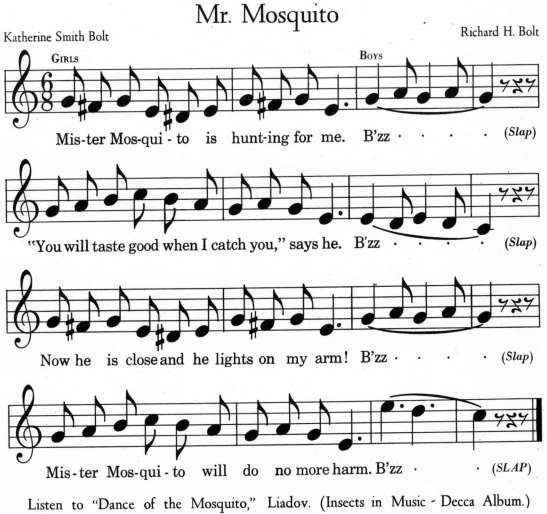

GIRLS

BOYS

Mis - ter Mos-qui - to   is   hunt-ing for me.   B'zz · · · ·   (Slap)

"You will taste good when I catch you," says he.   B'zz · · · ·   (Slap)

Now he   is close and he lights on my arm! B'zz · · · ·   (Slap)

Mis - ter Mos-qui - to   will   do   no more harm. B'zz · · ·   (SLAP)

Listen to "Dance of the Mosquito," Liadov. (Insects in Music - Decca Album.)

125

Funny Little Squirrel

V. M. S.

Verna Meade Surer

Fun-ny lit-tle squirrel, Run-ning up a tree,

You're fast, fast, fast as you can be.

Soon you will come down To see what you can find,

Then up and up you'll go With your bush-y tail be-hind.

Little Frog

N. B.

Nadine Bensley

Hop, hop, lit-tle frog, Fun-ny lit-tle fel-low on a log.

Jump, jump, oh, so high! If I were a frog, I think I'd try.

Pets

If I had a hundred dollars to spend,
Or maybe a little more,
I'd hurry as fast as my legs would go
Straight to the animal store.

I wouldn't say, "How much for this or that?"
"What kind of a dog is he?"
I'd buy as many as rolled an eye,
Or wagged a tail at me!

Rachel Field

Oh Where, Oh Where Has My Little Dog Gone?

German

Oh, where, oh where has my lit - tle dog gone,

Oh where, oh where can he be?

With his ears cut short and his tail cut long,

so   la   so   fa   mi   re   do

Oh where, oh where can he be?

127

Ding, Dong, Bell

Traditional

Ding, dong, bell, Puss-y's in the well;

Who put her in? Lit-tle John-ny Green.

so la ti do

Who took her out? Big Wil-lie Stout.

What a naught-y boy was that, To drown our lit-tle Puss-y-cat!

Cats and Dogs

Virginia Lynd Hartley

Czech Folk Tune

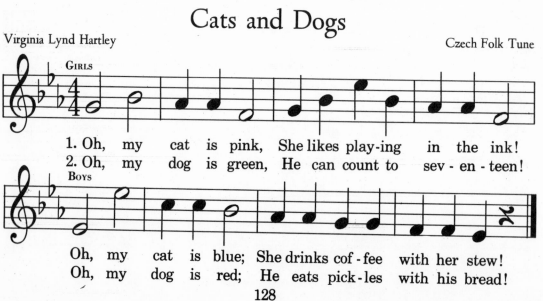

GIRLS

1. Oh, my cat is pink, She likes play-ing in the ink!
2. Oh, my dog is green, He can count to sev-en-teen!

BOYS

Oh, my cat is blue; She drinks cof-fee with her stew!
Oh, my dog is red; He eats pick-les with his bread!

Scat! Scat!

Grace B. Haynes

Joan Henry

so mi la so so fa mi

Scat! scat! you fun-ny old cat. Don't put your paws in my bat - ter.

re mi fa so la ti do do

Scat! scat! just stay on your mat, Don't try to get an - y fat - ter.

Listen to "Mi-a-ou" from *Dolly Suite*, Faure. (Columbia record.)

Little Dicky Bird

Marian Major

Richard Mertens

1. Lit - tle dick-y bird, lit - tle dick-y bird, Won't you sing a song for me?
2. Lit - tle dick-y bird, lit - tle dick-y bird, You are hap-py all the day.

I will give · you seeds and wa - ter, If you will but sing for me.
Sing a hap-py tune, sing it ver-y soon, Then you'll make the world more gay.

My Dog

My dog-gy's name is Spot and I love him such a lot.

He has two eyes and one is white, but one is not!

A Getting-Up Song

1. When cats get up in the morn-ing They al-ways say, "Good day,"
2. When dogs get up in the morn-ing They al-ways say, "Good day,"

When cats get up in the morn-ing They al-ways say, "Good day."
When dogs get up in the morn-ing They al-ways say, "Good day."

Meow! Meow! Meow! Meow! That is what they say, they say,
Bow wow! Bow wow! That is what they say, they say,

Meow! Meow! Meow! Meow! That is what they say.
Bow wow! Bow wow! That is what they say.

My Three Friends

Translated

French

I have three friends and I will name them,

Ro - cam - bo - le[1] and Jean[2] and Mi - net.[3]

They speak to me, now can you guess them

When I · tell you what they say?

Meow, meow, woof, woof, woof, woof, woof,

Hee - haw, hee - haw, hee - haw, hee - haw, hee - haw.

Pronounce: [1]row-kom-bow-le [2]zhawn [3]mee-nay

Shoe the Horse

Nursery Rhyme Charles Leonhard

Shoe the lit-tle horse and shoe the lit-tle mare,

And let the lit-tle colt-ie run, run bare, bare, bare.

I Had a Little Hobby-Horse

Nursery Rhyme L. B. P.

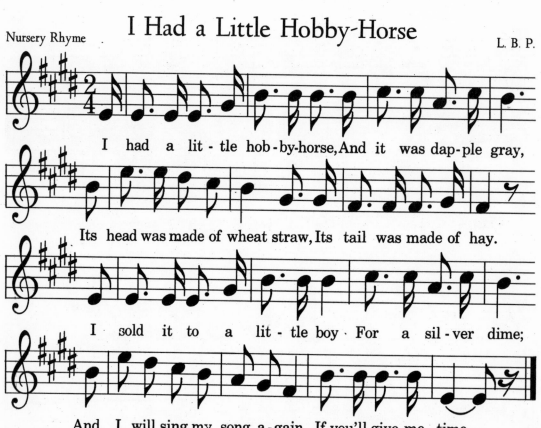

I had a lit-tle hob-by-horse, And it was dap-ple gray,

Its head was made of wheat straw, Its tail was made of hay.

I sold it to a lit-tle boy For a sil-ver dime;

And I will sing my song a-gain, If you'll give me time.

Listen to "Hobby Horse" from *Memories of Childhood*, Pinto. (Victor Listening Album One.)

132

Ride Away

Arranged from a
French Folk Tune

do mi re do mi re

Ride a - way, ride a - way, On my lit - tle po - ny gray.

A - walk, walk, walk, walk, walk, walk, walk.

Clap with hands cupped.

A - trot - trot, trot - trot, trot - trot, trot - trot, trot - trot, trot - trot, trot.

Clap with palms flat.

A - gal-lop-ing, gal-lop-ing, gal-lop-ing, gal-lop-ing, gal-lop-ing, gal-lop-ing, Whoa!

Clap with palms flat.

Listen to "High Stepping Horses," Anderson. (Victor Rhythm Album One.)

Ride Away

How many of you can play this piece on the piano with both hands?

133

On the Farm

When the farmer's day is done,
In the barnyard, every one,
Beast and bird politely say,
"Thank you for my food today."

When the barn is locked up tight,
Then the farmer says, "Good night!"
Thanks his animals, every one,
For the work that has been done.

Maude Burnham

The Barnyard

Maude Burnham

James Seton

do do mi so so la la so

The cow says, "Moo!" The pi-geon, "Coo!" The sheep says, "Baa!"

The lamb says, "Maa!" The hen, "Cluck, cluck!" "Quack," says the duck;

The dog, "Bow wow!" The cat, "Me-ow!" The horse says, "Neigh!

so fa fa mi re re re do

I love sweet hay!" The pig near-by Grunts in his sty.

Widdy-Widdy-Wurky

Lady Bell

From "Singing Circle"

do re mi fa so do

1. Wid - dy - wid - dy - wur - ky, I call my fat tur - key,
2. Wid - dy - wid - dy - wur - ky, I call my fat tur - key,

Sit - a - gain is my hen, Feath - er - loose is my goose,
Quack - y - wuck is my duck, Vel - vet - mat is my cat,

Wid - dy wid - dy - wur - ky, I call my fat tur - key.
Wid - dy wid - dy - wur - ky, I call my fat tur - key.

Dive, Ducks, Dive

Rowena B. Bennett

James Seton

do do

Dive, ducks, dive,   One, two, three, four, five,

Dip and dive and hur - ry back To the shore and leave a track

Of part - ing wa - ter at your back, Dive, ducks, dive.

Donkey

Nursery Rhyme

Paul Forde

Don-key, don-key old and gray, O-pen your mouth and loud-ly bray,

Lift your ears and blow your horn, To wake up the world this sleep-y morn.

Hee - haw, · hee-haw, · hee - haw, hee-haw, hee - haw.

Go Tell Aunt Nancy

American Play Party Song

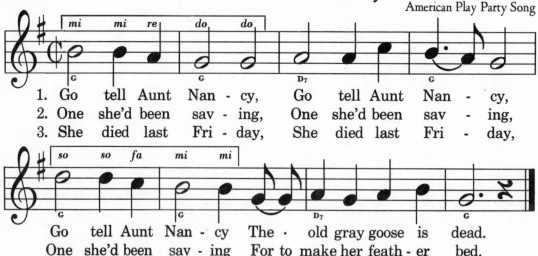

1. Go tell Aunt Nan - cy, Go tell Aunt Nan - cy,
2. One she'd been sav - ing, One she'd been sav - ing,
3. She died last Fri - day, She died last Fri - day,

Go tell Aunt Nan - cy The · old gray goose is dead.
One she'd been sav - ing For to make her feath - er bed.
She died last Fri - day With a pain all in her head.

4. Old gander's weeping,
   Old gander's weeping,
   Old gander's weeping
   Because his wife is dead.

5. Goslings are mourning,
   Goslings are mourning,
   Goslings are mourning
   Because their mother's dead.

136

Laughing, Ho, Ho!

Carol Fuller

French Folk Tune

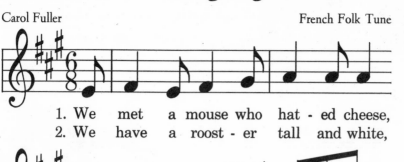

1. We met a mouse who hat - ed cheese,
2. We have a roost - er tall and white,

He was so hard to please. Mous-ie, ho, ho!
Who likes to crow all night. Roost-er, ho, ho!

Ah, ha, ha, ha! Oh, what a fun - ny mouse you are, you are!
Ah, ha, ha, ha! Oh, what a nois - y bird you are, you are!

My Black Hen

Nursery Rhyme

Susan Castle

Hick - e -ty pick -e - ty, my black hen, She lays eggs for gen - tle-men,

Some-times nine and some-times ten, Hick-e -ty pick -e - ty, my black hen.

Ku-Ku-Ri-Ku![1]

Translated

Jewish

so so la so fa mi mi re re do

Ku - ku - ri - ku, the roost - er calls at morn,

Ku - ku - ri - ku, the roost - er calls at morn.

mi so do

Get up, girls, get up, boys, get up, girls and boys!

Get up, girls, get up, boys, get up, girls and boys!

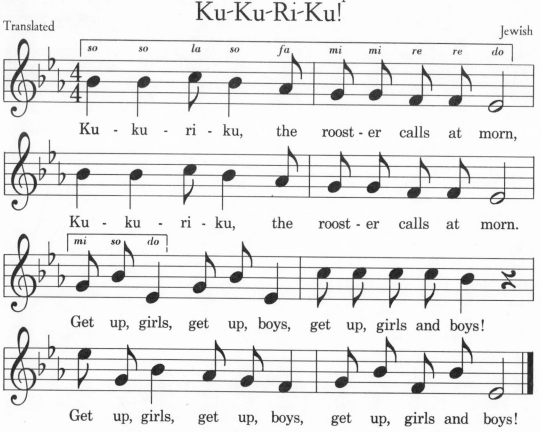

[1] Pronounce: koo-koo-ree-koo.

Little Baby Duckies

L. B.

Lydia Boothby

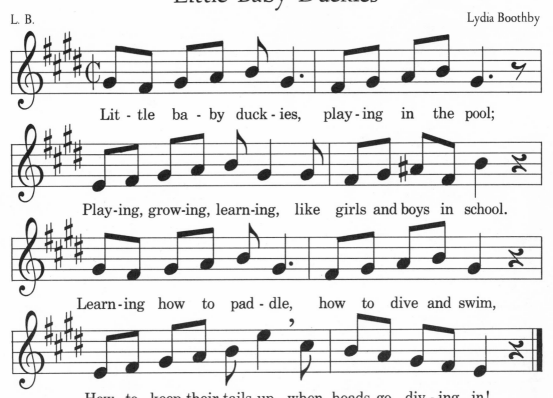

Lit - tle ba - by duck - ies, play - ing in the pool;

Play-ing, grow-ing, learn-ing, like girls and boys in school.

Learn-ing how to pad - dle, how to dive and swim,

How to keep their tails up when heads go div - ing in!

Little Boy Blue

Mother Goose

Traditional

Lit - tle Boy Blue, come blow ·· your horn,

The sheep's in the mead-ow, the cow's in the corn;

Where is the boy who looks aft - er the sheep?

so fa mi re do

He's un - der the hay - stack fast a - sleep.

Little Bo-Peep

Mother Goose

J. W. Elliott

Lit-tle Bo-peep has lost her sheep, And can't tell where to find them;

do ti la so mi do re do

Leave them a-lone, and they'll come home, Wag-ging their tails be - hind them.

140

ABOUT SINGING THINGS

When I was young
I dared to sing
Of everything
And anything!

James Stephens

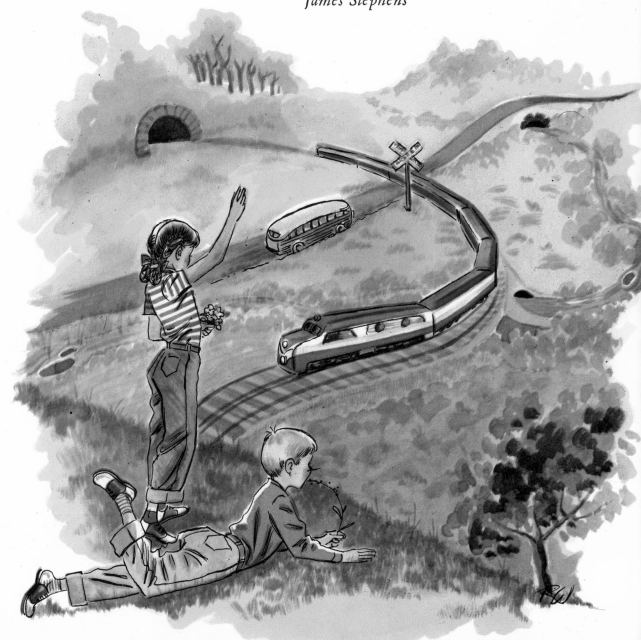

Things That Sing at Home

Tick Tock

L. B. P.

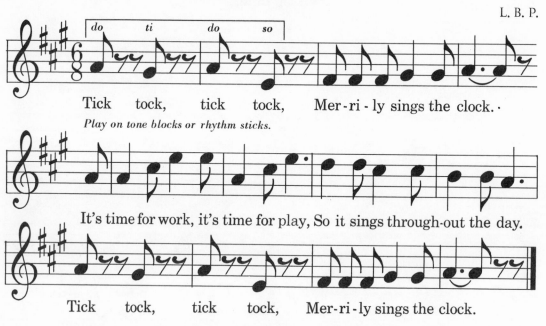

Tick tock, tick tock, Mer-ri-ly sings the clock.

Play on tone blocks or rhythm sticks.

It's time for work, it's time for play, So it sings through-out the day.

Tick tock, tick tock, Mer-ri-ly sings the clock.

Listen to "The Clock," Kullak. (Victor Rhythm Album Three.)

The Sweeper Song

M. M.

Marian Major

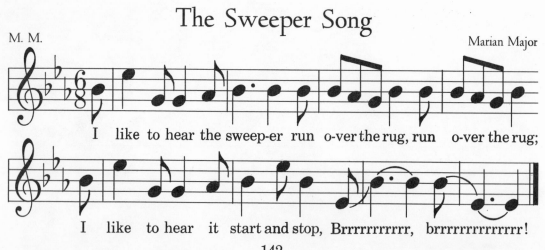

I like to hear the sweep-er run o-ver the rug, run o-ver the rug;

I like to hear it start and stop, Brrrrrrrrrrr, brrrrrrrrrrrrrrr!

142

The Lawn Mower Song

Marian Major

M. M.

I like to hear the mow - er, Ric - a-tic-a-tic, ric-a-tic-a-tic,

(How does your mower sing?)

As it goes fast and slow - er, Ric-a - tic-a-tic-a-tic-a - tic - tic - tic.

The whirl-ing blades are bright and keen; It leaves our lawn all smooth and green.

I like to hear the mow - er, Ric - a-tic-a-tic, ric-a-tic-a-tic,

Ric - a - tic-a-tic-a-tic- a - tic - tic - tic.

The Ice Box Song

Marian Major

M. M.

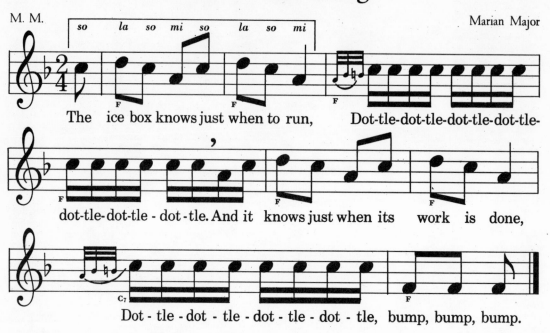

so la so mi so la so mi

The ice box knows just when to run, Dot-tle-dot-tle-dot-tle-dot-tle-

dot-tle-dot-tle - dot-tle. And it knows just when its work is done,

Dot - tle - dot - tle - dot - tle - dot-tle, bump, bump, bump.

The Telephone Song

Marian Major

M. M.

do do do do do , so do

Ting-a-ling-a-ling! Hel - lo! Ting-a-ling-a-ling! Hel - lo!

When the tel - e - phone is ring-ing, I'm the one who runs to an-swer.

Ting-a-ling-a-ling! Hel - lo! Ting -a-ling-a-ling! Hel - lo!

You never know with a doorbell
Who may be ringing it—
Doorbells are like a magic game,
Or the grab-bag at a fair—
You never know when you hear one ring
Who may be waiting there!

Rachel Field

Knock, Knock!

Marian Major

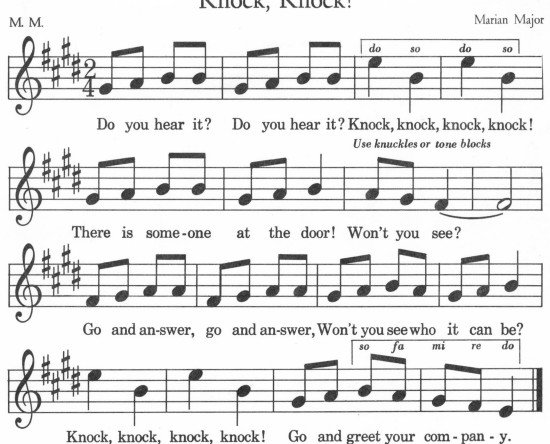

Do you hear it?   Do you hear it? Knock, knock, knock, knock!

Use knuckles or tone blocks

There is some-one   at   the door! Won't you see?

Go and an-swer, go and an-swer, Won't you see who it can be?

Knock, knock, knock, knock!   Go and greet your com - pan - y.

The Faucet Song

M. M.

Marian Major

The wa-ter fau-cet is sing-ing a song,

so *mi*

Bleep, bloop, bleep, bloop, bleep, bloop, bleep, bloop.

Its mer-ry mu-sic goes sing-ing a-long,

Bleep, bloop, bleep, bloop, bleep, bloop.

146

Bells

Sing, you rimes, and ring, you chimes,
And swing, and ring, and rime!

Nancy Byrd Turner

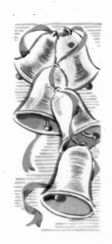

Bells

Hear the bells in the tow'r Sweet-ly ring and tell the hour.

The Bell Doth Toll

Old Round

The bell doth toll, its ech-oes roll, I know the sound full well;

I love its ring-ing, for it calls to sing-ing

With its bim, bim, bim bom, bell. Bim! Bom! Bim, bom, bell.

Strike large bell or gong.

Listen to "Evening Bells," Kullak. (Victor Listening Album Two.)

Trains, Planes, and Other Things

The train begins to move along,
The wheels begin to make a song
Speeding along on the long, long track
Clicket-a-clacket, a-clacket, a-clack
Go the wheels of the passenger train.

Edith H. Newlin

Here Is a Big Train

Ding, ding, ding, dong, Choo choo, choo choo, Here is a big train,

Choo choo, choo choo, Run-ning down the track.

Choo-ka, choo-ka, choo-ka, choo-ka, choo-ka, choo-ka, choo-ka, choo-ka,

Click-e-ty clack, click-e-ty clack, click-e-ty click-e-ty clack.

"Running Horses," Anderson (Victor Rhythm Album One) is good rhythm for playing train.

148

Taking Off

Mary McB. Green

Francis Hilliard

The air-plane tax - is down the field And heads in - to the breeze,

It lifts its wheels a - bove the ground, It skims a - bove the trees, ·

It ris - es high and high - er A - way up toward the sun, ·

It's just a speck a-gainst the sky And now it's gone! ·

Play "airplanes" when listening to "Run, Run, Run," Concone. (Victor Rhythm
Album Two.)

Here We Go a-Riding on a Train

Children's Song

Ding, ding, ding, ding, ding, ding, ding! All a-board, all a-board!

slow

Too-too-too-too! Choo, choo, choo, choo, choo, choo, choo, choo!

a little faster

Here we go a-rid-ing on a train.

Here we go a-rid-ing on a train.

faster

Down the track click-i-ty clack, Down the track click-i-ty clack,

Here we go a-rid-ing on a train.

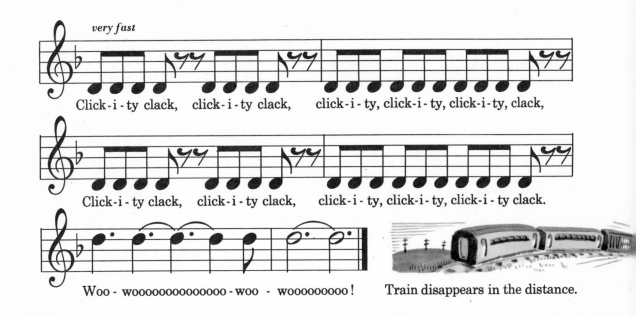

very fast

Click-i-ty clack, click-i-ty clack, click-i-ty, click-i-ty, click-i-ty, clack,

Click-i-ty clack, click-i-ty clack, click-i-ty, click-i-ty, click-i-ty clack.

Woo - woooooooooooooo - woo - woooooooooo! Train disappears in the distance.

The Cars Go Up and Down

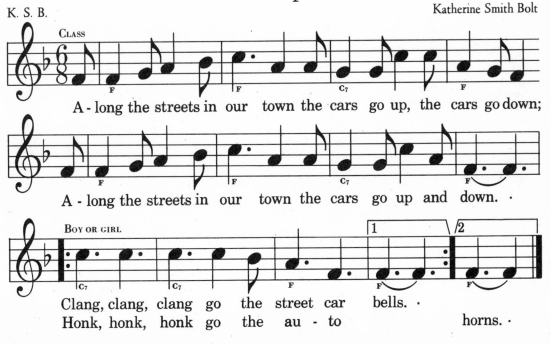

K. S. B.

Katherine Smith Bolt

CLASS

A - long the streets in our town the cars go up, the cars go down;

A - long the streets in our town the cars go up and down.

BOY OR GIRL

Clang, clang, clang go the street car bells. ·
Honk, honk, honk go the au - to horns. ·

(Sing about the things that go up and down your street.)

151

The Motor Boat

Nadine Bensley

N. B.

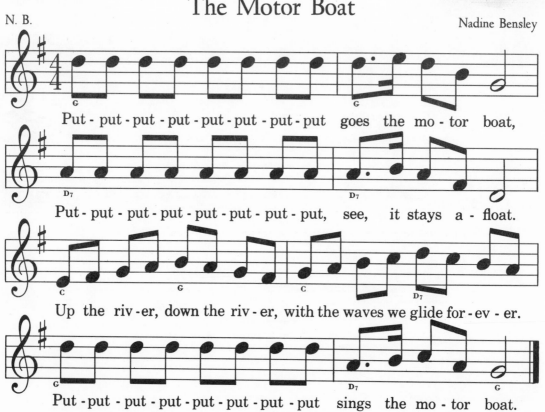

Put - put - put - put - put - put - put - put goes the mo - tor boat,

Put - put - put - put - put - put - put - put, see, it stays a - float.

Up the riv - er, down the riv - er, with the waves we glide for - ev - er.

Put - put - put - put - put - put - put - put sings the mo - tor boat.

152

The Bus

Play Song

1. The peo-ple on the bus go   up   and down,
2. The wheels on the bus go   round and round,
3. The horn   on the bus goes too, too, too,
4. The mon-ey in the box goes ding, ding, ding,

Up   and down, up   and down.
Round and round, round and round.
Too, too, too,   too, too, too.
Ding, ding, ding, ding, ding, ding.

The   peo-ple on the bus go   up   and down,
The   wheels on the bus go   round and round,
The   horn   on the bus goes too, too, too,
The   mon-ey in the box goes ding, ding, ding,

1, 2, 3, 4. All   through   the   town.

5. The wiper on the glass goes swish, swish, swish,
   Swish, swish, swish, swish, swish, swish.
   The wiper on the glass goes swish, swish, swish,
   All through the town.

6. The driver on the bus says, "Move on back,
   Move on back, move on back."
   The driver on the bus says, "Move on back."
   All through the town.

153

We Play and Sing

Our Band

Italian

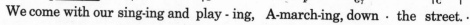

We come with our sing-ing and play - ing, A-march-ing, down · the street. ·

Now what can the mu - sic be say - ing To our march - ing feet? ·

Rat- ta - ta - tat, rat-ta - ta - tat, Hear how the snare drums play rat - ta - ta - tat.
Ta - ta - ta - ta, ta - ta - ta - ta, Hear how the trom-bone plays ta - ta - ta - ta.
Too-too-too-toot, too-too-too-toot, Hear how the trum-pet plays too-too-too-toot.

Amaryllis

Henri Ghys

Listen to "Amaryllis," Ghys. (Victor Rhythm Band Album.) This is a good piece to accompany with rhythm instruments. Listen for this tune as you play them.

154

Playing a Tune

G. H.

Graham Haswell

1. I can play a tune on the xy - lo - phone,
2. We can play three tones on the xy - lo - phone,

Do re mi mi mi mi re do do do.
1 2 3 3 3 3 2 1 1 1.

This song can be played on the piano, and water glasses also.

Ring, Ring

G. H.

Graham Haswell

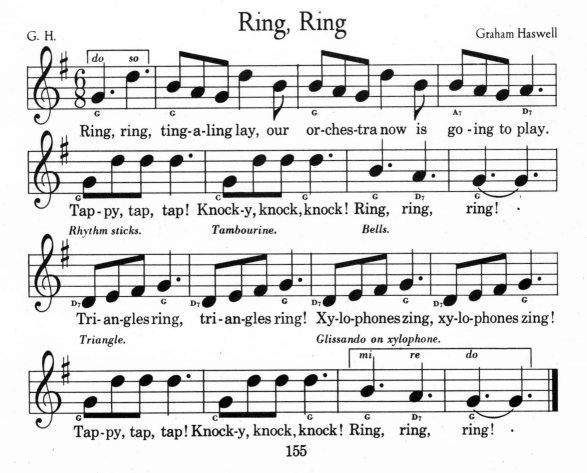

Ring, ring, ting-a-ling lay, our or-ches-tra now is go-ing to play.

Tap-py, tap, tap! Knock-y, knock, knock! Ring, ring, ring!

Rhythm sticks.   *Tambourine.*   *Bells.*

Tri-an-gles ring, tri-an-gles ring! Xy-lo-phones zing, xy-lo-phones zing!

Triangle.   *Glissando on xylophone.*

Tap-py, tap, tap! Knock-y, knock, knock! Ring, ring, ring!

155

I Can Play and Sing

1. I can play a lit - tle tune, lit - tle tune, lit - tle tune,
2. 1 2 3 4 5 5 5, 4 3 2 3 4 5,
3. g a b c d d d makes a tune, you can see.

Do re mi fa so so so, fa mi re do.
When I play, I sing a song All the day long.
Sing these pret - ty notes to me, c b a g.

This tune can be played on the piano, the xylophone and water glasses.

Shadows

Ludwig Schytte

1. Do so la ti do so la ti do do ti ti la la so.
2. 8 5 6 7 8 5 6 7 8 8 7 7 6 6 5.

Listen to "Shadows," Schytte. (Victor Rhythm Band Album.) This also is a good piece to accompany rhythm band instruments. See if you know when this tune comes on the record.

Hear the Bells

Austrian

Hear the bells, hear their song.

Ding ding dong, ding ding dong; Ding dong, ding dong.

One of you can play this song on the piano with both hands while others sing it or play it on bells.

Morning Bells

Lena Chase

Folk Tune

Some of you may play this song on melody bells as others sing.

Morn-ing bells are gai-ly ring-ing, Ding dong, ding dong;

High up in the bel-fry swing-ing, Dong, ding dong.

Silver Bells

Ethel Crowninshield

Carinthian Folk Tune

Ding ding ding, sil - ver bells sing a song.

Ding ding ding, plain - ly I hear.

Ding ding ding, now it is far a - way;

Ding ding ding, now it is near.

The Fiddles

Louise Ayres Garnett

Ludwig van Beethoven

1. Sweet and clear, far and near, Sweet - ly fid - dles are play - ing;
2. Sweet and clear you can hear What the fid - dles are say - ing;

Sum - mer night, stars are bright; You must fol - low the sound.
Make a ring, dance and sing, Round and round and a - round!

You will enjoy playing these two songs on melody bells.

Riding on My Pony

L. P. H.

Lithuanian Folk Tune

Clip clop clip clop   clip clop clip clop.
(Play "hoof beats" on wood blocks throughout song.)

Rid-ing on my po-ny,   Trot trot trot trot   trot-ting

On the trail so lone-ly,   Trot trot trot trot   trot-ting.

Har-ness bells are gai-ly ring-ing, Jin-gle jan-gle, gai-ly ring-ing;
(Add bells.)

Jog-ging down the moun-tain.   *Clip clop clip clop clip clop clip clop.*
(Hoof beats fade away.)

159

The Bells

Lucy Allen

Will Earhart

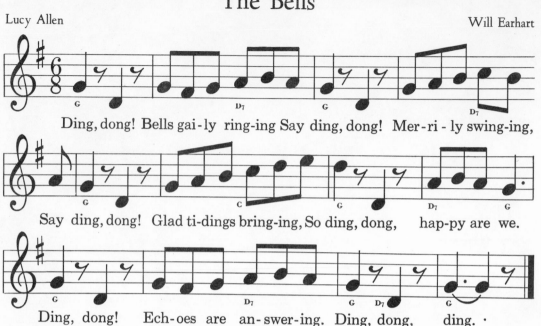

Ding, dong! Bells gai-ly ring-ing Say ding, dong! Mer-ri-ly swing-ing,

Say ding, dong! Glad ti-dings bring-ing, So ding, dong, hap-py are we.

Ding, dong! Ech-oes are an-swer-ing. Ding, dong, ding. ·

Fairy Voices

English version by
Frederick H. Martens

Russian Folk Song

1. Fair-y voic-es, sweet and light, Soft-ly fall-ing on the night,
2. Fair-y voic-es, far a-way, How I won-der what you say!

Like some sil-ver gong Rings a hap-py fair-y song.
Soon your mu-sic dies Un-der-neath the qui-et skies.

Like some sil-ver gong Rings a hap-py fair-y song.
Soon your mu-sic dies Un-der-neath the qui-et skies.

Carnival

by

Elizabeth E. Rogers

We are going to a carnival today! John and Mary,
Sue and Tommy, everyone is going. You come too!

Bells play introduction.

Triangles

1. We won - der, we won - der, We won-der what we'll see.
2. We won - der, we won - der, We won-der what we'll do.

Add rhythm sticks

Come a - long and take a seat, The price, you know, is ver - y cheap!
Take a ride or see a show. Oh hur - ry, hur-ry, here we go!

Add tambourines

1,2. Car - ni - vals are such a lot of fun, fun, fun;

Car - ni - vals are such a lot of fun!

Oh look! Here comes the parade.

March tempo
Band enters, all instruments playing.

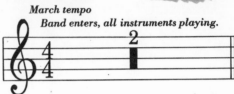

1. Hear the mu - sic play - ing, hear the drums a - beat - ing,
2. Let us join the mu - sic, let us join the play - ing,

Hear the cym - bals say - ing, "Car - ni - val."
Let us join the danc - ing, "Car - ni - val."

1,2. Hear the horns a - toot - ing, hear the flutes a - flut - ing,

Hear the bark - er root - ing, "Car - ni - val."

162

There's a man in a tall hat! See him over there!
He's the ticket seller. He's telling us to hurry.

Drums

Hur - ry,   hur - ry,   hur - ry!

Rhythm sticks and cymbals

Hur - ry,   hur - ry!   Who will   be   the   first?
Hur - ry,   hur - ry!   Who will   be   the   next?

Hi there,   son - ny!   You may   be   the   first.
Hi there,   miss - y!   You shall be   the   next.

I've   a   long roll   of tick-ets, Quite e - nough for ev - 'ry - one.
I've   a   long roll   of tick-ets, But they're go-ing ver - y   fast.

Won't you hur-ry, hur-ry, hur-ry So you don't miss the fun!
Won't you hur-ry, hur-ry, hur-ry While the tick - ets do last!

163

See the balloon man with a whole armful of balloons.
He's waiting for us!

Red bal - loons, yel - low bal - loons,

All of them reach - ing for the sky.

Green bal - loons, pur - ple bal - loons,

All on a string that floats so high.

Here's one for John and one for Lou, One for Ter-ry and one for you.

Come buy, · come buy, · Come buy! · ·

164

What's that we hear? It's the merry-go-round.
Let's take a ride.

Wood blocks
and
jingle bells.

1. Li - ons and ti - gers go 'round and 'round.
2. Zing - a - ling, zing - a - ling, bells do sing
3. 'Round and a - round and a - round we go,

The or - ches - tra plays with an off - key sound
As some - bod - y catch - es the gold - en ring.
So fast and so fast, and so slow, so slow.

As hors - es prance and ze - bras dance
An - oth - er ride, an ex - tra turn
Pick out your place, get set, let's go

1,2,3. On the mer - ry - go, mer - ry - go - round and round,

On the mer - ry - go, mer - ry - go - round.

165

Listen! Over here is a barker. Isn't he funny!
"Step right up to the biggest, little, side-front-back-
and-all-around show in the world."

Triangles, Cymbals, Rhythm Sticks,
Shakers, Drums

This way to the side show, step right in!

This way to the side show, step right in!

Look at all there is to see, walk right in, it's all for free.

Hur - ry, hur - ry, hur - ry to the big side show!

166

There's a strong man who is strong,

And a brave fire-eat-er too.

There are man-y, man-y an-i-mals you won't find in a zoo!

There's a clown who real-ly clowns,

And a tat-tooed sail-or too,

There is Punch and there is Ju-dy And the fun-ny things they do.

Have you ever thrown a ring over a cane? Come on, who will try?

1. Ring a cane, (click, click, click) Ring a cane, (click, click, click)
2. Toss a coin, (ching, ching, ching) Toss a coin, (ching, ching, ching)
3. Catch a fish, (swish, swish, swish) Catch a fish, (swish, swish, swish)

The cane you ring, the cane you get,
You toss a pen-ny on the square,
You catch a fish and choose a prize,

The cane you car-ry home, you bet!
And you will win a wool-ly bear!
Yes, an-y col-or, an-y size!

Ring a cane, (click, click, click) Ring a luck-y, luck-y cane!
Toss a coin, (ching, ching, ching) Toss a luck-y, luck-y coin!
Catch a fish, (swish, swish, swish) Catch a luck-y, luck-y fish!

Play instruments:
1. *Wood blocks* and *rhythm sticks* for "clicks."
2. *Bells* and *triangles* for "chings."
3. *Sand blocks* and *washboards* for "swishes."

That was a lot of fun, but I'm hungry! We're all hungry!

Maracas, shakers, etc.

Pop-corn, so-da, crack-er-jack,

One for a nick-el, two for a dime!

Cot-ton can-dy on a stick,

One for a nick-el, two for a dime!

Ice cream cones and can-dy too,

Pop-si-cles and gum to chew,

All of them are just for you And now is the time.

169

Carnivals are lots of fun, but now it is time to go. Let's sing on our way home.

Play all instruments.

Hear the mu-sic play-ing, hear the drums a-beat-ing,

Hear the cym-bals say-ing, "Car - ni - val."

Hear the horns a-toot-ing, hear the flutes a-flut-ing,

Hear the bark-er root-ing, "Car - ni - val."

THE END

SHINING HOURS

The Shoemaker and the Elves

By Frank Luther

This is the story of the shoemaker and the elves.

[Recorded on Decca record No. C.U.S. 8]

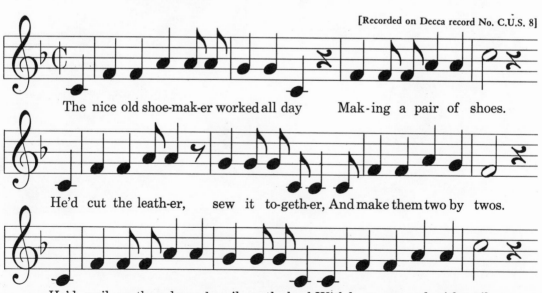

The nice old shoe-mak-er worked all day   Mak-ing a pair of shoes.

He'd cut the leath-er,   sew it to-geth-er, And make them two by twos.

He'd nail on the sole, and nail on the heel With ham-mer and with nail,

With a rap, tap, tap, *(Tap on desk with forefinger.)* Rap, tap, tap

And the shoes were read-y for sale, sale, sale, And the shoes were read-y for sale.

But the nice old shoemaker grew poorer and poorer, until one day there was no food in the house, and he had only enough leather to make one pair of shoes. So he cut out the leather, ready to make the shoes in the morning, and before he went to bed he said his prayers.

Lord, help us to be good, Lord, help us to be good.

Help us to love each oth - er, Then we will help each oth - er.

Lord, help us to be good.

Early the next morning the shoemaker woke up, and there were the shoes, already made! He sold the shoes for enough money to buy leather for *two* pairs of shoes.

So he cut the leather ready to make the shoes in the morning, and before he went to bed he said his prayers.

Early the next morning the shoemaker woke up, and there were the shoes, already made! He sold the shoes for enough money to buy leather for *eight* pairs of shoes.

This went on until the nice old shoemaker and his wife became rich.

Still they didn't know who came in the middle of the night and made the shoes. One day his wife said, "Tonight let's watch and see who makes the shoes for us."

So that night the old shoemaker cut the leather, put it on the bench; then the old shoemaker and his wife watched and they waited. And on the stroke of midnight—Look!

Here came five little elves! They hopped on the shoemaker's bench. They took out their needles and their tiny little hammers, and they began to make the shoes.

We are five lit-tle elves   Named [1]Al - fun, El - fun, Il - fun, Ol - fun, Ul - fun.   We make the shoes our - selves;

[1]Pronounce the first letters of the elves' names as vowel sounds: a, e, i, o, u.

I mean Āl - fun, Ēl - fun, Īl - fun, Ōl - fun, Ūl - fun.

We ham-mer, ham-mer, ham-mer, ham-mer, stitch and stitch.

We hop and wig - gle and laugh and gig - gle and

work all night 'til broad day-light. We are five lit - tle elves

Named Āl - fun, Ēl - fun, Īl - fun, Ōl - fun, Ūl - fun.

When the shoes were all done, the five little elves hopped off the bench, hopped out the door, and away they went over the hill.

The good shoemaker's wife said, "How kind the little elves are to make the shoes for us! Now, what can we do for them?"

The good shoemaker said, "I'll make them new shoes." His wife said, "I'll make little trousers for them, and little pink caps and little blue coats with little brass buttons."

And they did!

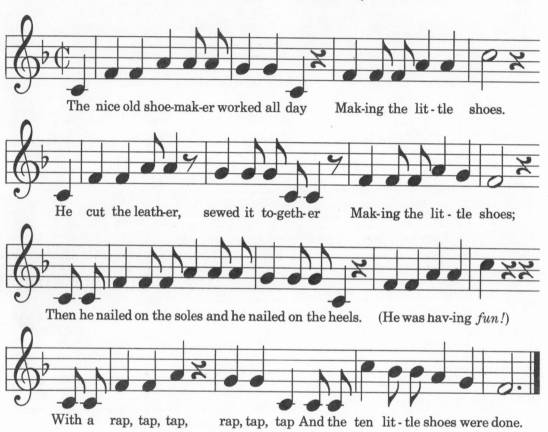

The nice old shoe-mak-er worked all day Mak-ing the lit-tle shoes.

He cut the leath-er, sewed it to-geth-er Mak-ing the lit-tle shoes;

Then he nailed on the soles and he nailed on the heels. (He was hav-ing *fun!*)

With a rap, tap, tap, rap, tap, tap And the ten lit-tle shoes were done.

The good shoemaker's wife started to work.

She made lit-tle trou-sers red as red

Out of a piece of an old bed-spread.

"My," she said, "but they are nice and red."

She made lit-tle caps as pink as pink. Shine so bright that they

make you blink. "My, I think that noth-ing's pink as pink!"

She made lit-tle coats as blue as blue, Bright brass but-tons two by two.

"My, but I like new blue coats, don't you?"

When they were all done, the shoe-maker's wife took the little trousers and caps and coats and laid them on the shoemaker's bench. The shoemaker put the ten little shoes beside them. (I forgot to tell you it was Christmas Eve.) So they wrote five little notes that said, "Merry Christmas, little Elf," and put the notes with the presents.

Snow was falling in big, soft fluffy flakes. The bells were ringing and all the children were safe in their beds, dreaming of toys and Santa Claus.

Then the clock struck the hour of midnight. Look!

In came the five little elves. They saw the red trousers, the pink caps, the little blue coats and the little black shoes. They just stood there with their little mouths open—and looked—and looked!

Then they started to laugh. They started to sing and jump up and down and slap each other on the back and say, "Look at our Christmas presents! They must be from the good shoemaker and his wife!"

They put the lit-tle red trou-sers on. (Left leg first, then the right.)

They put the lit-tle black shoes on. (Left shoe first, then the right.)

They put the lit-tle blue coats on. (Not too big, not too tight.)

They put the lit-tle pink caps on. They were a won-der-ful sight.

Then the five little elves hopped down off the shoemaker's bench, hopped out the door and away they went
over the hill, laughing and singing:

Mer - ry, Mer - ry Christ - mas to the good shoe - mak - er,

And the good shoe - mak - er's wife.

Mer - ry, Mer - ry Christ - mas, Fa - thers and Moth - ers,

And all the girls and boys.

The Three Billy Goats Gruff

By Frank Luther

This is the story of the Three Billy Goats Gruff.

[Recorded on Decca record No. C.U.S. 10]

On a bluff, on a bluff There lived Three Bil-ly Goats Gruff.

(high voice) *(middle voice)* *(heavy voice)*

(Lit - tle Bil - ly Goat, Mid - dle Bil - ly Goat, Great Big Bil - ly Goat Gruff.)

Ev-'ry day, ev-'ry day They'd run and jump and play,

(high voice) (middle voice) (heavy voice)

(Lit-tle Bil-ly Goat, Mid-dle Bil-ly Goat Great Big Bil-ly Goat Gruff.)

They'd run and run and run and run And run and run and run;

They'd hop and hop and hop and hop You'd think they'd nev-er stop!

On a bluff, on a bluff There lived Three Bil-ly Goats Gruff.

(high voice) (middle voice) (heavy voice)

(Lit-tle Bil-ly Goat, Mid-dle Bil-ly Goat, Great Big Bil-ly Goat Gruff.)

Across the river bridge was a meadow full of green, green grass. Under the bridge lived a big, bad troll, and all day long he'd sit under the bridge and sing his big, bad troll song.

Drolly, trollily (clownishly, half-laughing)

"I'm a troll, · (Foll de roll)   I'm a troll, · (Foll de roll)
I've three heads and I've three hats,   I've three chins and I've three cats,

I'm a troll, · (Foll de roll,   Foll de roll de roll-y.) ·
I've six eyes and I've six ears,   When I cry   I   cry six tears."

One day the Three Billy Goats Gruff ate the last of the grass on their bluff; so they decided to go over the bridge to the green, green meadow with the red, red roses, where they could eat the green, green grass until they nearly burst.

So Little Billy Goat Gruff started trip trap, trip trap over the rickety, rackety bridge.

Lightly (little high voice)

Trip   trap,   trip   trap,   Hop and skip,   hop and skip.

But just when he reached the middle of the bridge the big, bad troll stuck his head up and said, "Who's that trip-trapping over my bridge?" Little Billy Goat Gruff said, "It is I, Little Billy Goat Gruff." The big, bad troll said,

"I'm a troll, (Foll de roll)   I'm a troll, (Foll de roll)

I'm a troll, (Foll de roll) And I'll eat you for sup-per." ·

The Little Billy Goat Gruff said, "Oh, Mr. Troll, I'm so little I wouldn't make even a sandwich for you. Wait for my brother who's coming right behind. He's much bigger than I am."

Well, the big, bad troll said he would.

So Little Billy Goat Gruff went trip trap, trip trap over the rickety, rackety bridge.

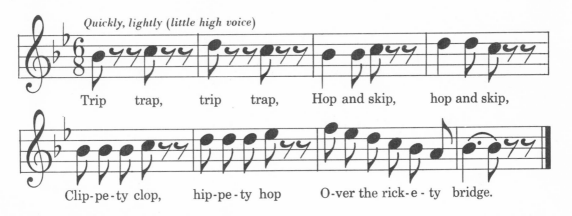

Quickly, lightly (little high voice)

Trip trap, trip trap, Hop and skip, hop and skip,

Clip-pe-ty clop, hip-pe-ty hop O-ver the rick-e-ty bridge.

When Little Billy Goat Gruff was safely across the bridge, Middle Billy Goat Gruff started trip trap, trip trap over the rickety, rackety bridge.

Moderately (middle voice)

Trip trap, trip trap, Hop and skip, hop and skip.

But just when he reached the middle of the bridge
the big, bad troll stuck his head up and said, "Who's
that trip-trapping over my bridge?" The goat said, "It
is I, Middle Billy Goat Gruff." The troll said,

"I'm a troll, (Foll de roll)   I'm a troll, (Foll de roll)

I'm a troll, (Foll de roll) And I'll eat you for sup-per."

The Middle Billy Goat Gruff said,
"Oh, Mr. Troll, I'm so little I wouldn't
make even a mouthful for you. Wait
for my brother who's coming right
behind. He's much bigger than I am."

The big, bad troll said he would.

So Middle Billy Goat Gruff went
trip trap, trip trap over the rickety,
rackety bridge.

Trip trap, trip trap, Hop and skip, hop and skip,

Clip-pe-ty clop, hip-pe-ty hop O-ver the rick-e-ty bridge.

When Middle Billy Goat Gruff was safely over the bridge, the Great Big Billy Goat Gruff started trip trap, trip trap over the rickety, rackety bridge.

But just when he reached the middle of the bridge the big, bad troll stuck his head up and said, "Who's that trip-trapping over my bridge?" The goat said, "It is I, Great Big Billy Goat Gruff."

The troll said,

"I'm a troll, (Foll de roll) I'm a troll, (Foll de roll)

I'm a troll, (Foll de roll) And I'll eat you for sup-per." ·

But Great Big Billy Goat Gruff said, "Oh no, you won't, Mr. Troll."

And Great Big Billy Goat Gruff put his head down, . . . (Baa) . . . he put his horns out, . . . (Baa) . . . And he ran clickety clackety, rickety rackety, slam bang, and he hit that big, bad troll . . . and knocked him over the bridge, . . . over the bushes, . . . over the trees, . . . over the hills, . . . over the highest mountains. . . .

So Great Big Billy Goat Gruff went trip trap, trip trap over the rickety, rackety bridge.

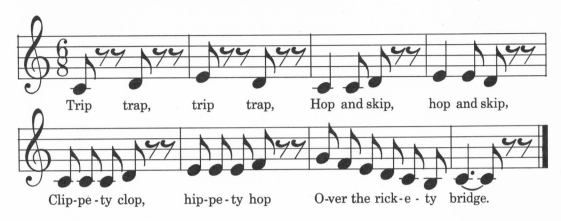

Trip trap, trip trap, Hop and skip, hop and skip,

Clip-pe-ty clop, hip-pe-ty hop O-ver the rick-e-ty bridge.

And so the Three Billy Goats Gruff were over in the green, green meadow with the red, red roses, eating the green, green grass until they nearly burst— and the big, bad troll never bothered them again.

And they are the happiest Billy Goats Gruff you ever saw.

Ev-'ry day, ev-'ry day They run and jump and play,
(high voice) (middle voice) (heavy voice)

Lit-tle Bil-ly Goat, Mid-dle Bil-ly Goat, Great Big Bil-ly Goat Gruff.

ALPHABETICAL INDEX

JKLM 069876
PRINTED IN THE UNITED STATES OF AMERICA